Student Edition

Eureka Math
Grade 7
Modules 3 & 4

Special thanks go to the Gordon A. Cain Center and to the Department of Mathematics at Louisiana State University for their support in the development of *Eureka Math*.

For a free *Eureka Math* Teacher Resource Pack, Parent Tip Sheets, and more please visit www.Eureka.tools

Published by the non-profit Great Minds

Copyright © 2015 Great Minds. No part of this work may be reproduced, sold, or commercialized, in whole or in part, without written permission from Great Minds. Non-commercial use is licensed pursuant to a Creative Commons Attribution-NonCommercial-ShareAlike 4.0 license; for more information, go to http://greatminds.net/maps/math/copyright. "Great Minds" and "Eureka Math" are registered trademarks of Great Minds.

Printed in the U.S.A.

This book may be purchased from the publisher at eureka-math.org

10 9

ISBN 978-1-63255-317-1

Lesson 1: Generating Equivalent Expressions

Classwork

Opening Exercise

Each envelope contains a number of triangles and a number of quadrilaterals. For this exercise, let t represent the number of triangles, and let q represent the number of quadrilaterals.

   a. Write an expression using t and q that represents the total number of sides in your envelope. Explain what the terms in your expression represent.

   b. You and your partner have the same number of triangles and quadrilaterals in your envelopes. Write an expression that represents the total number of sides that you and your partner have. If possible, write more than one expression to represent this total.

   c. Each envelope in the class contains the same number of triangles and quadrilaterals. Write an expression that represents the total number of sides in the room.

   d. Use the given values of t and q and your expression from part (a) to determine the number of sides that should be found in your envelope.

Lesson 1:   Generating Equivalent Expressions   S.1

© 2015 Great Minds. eureka-math.org
G7-M3M4-SE-B2-1.3.1-02.2016

e. Use the same values for t and q and your expression from part (b) to determine the number of sides that should be contained in your envelope and your partner's envelope combined.

f. Use the same values for t and q and your expression from part (c) to determine the number of sides that should be contained in all of the envelopes combined.

g. What do you notice about the various expressions in parts (e) and (f)?

Example 1: Any Order, Any Grouping Property with Addition

a. Rewrite $5x + 3x$ and $5x - 3x$ by combining like terms.

Write the original expressions and expand each term using addition. What are the new expressions equivalent to?

b. Find the sum of $2x + 1$ and $5x$.

EUREKA
MATH™

c.   Find the sum of $-3a + 2$ and $5a - 3$.

Example 2: Any Order, Any Grouping with Multiplication

Find the product of $2x$ and 3.

Example 3: Any Order, Any Grouping in Expressions with Addition and Multiplication

Use any order, any grouping to write equivalent expressions.

a. $3(2x)$

b. $4y(5)$

c. $4 \cdot 2 \cdot z$

d. $3(2x) + 4y(5)$

e. $3(2x) + 4y(5) + 4 \cdot 2 \cdot z$

f.   Alexander says that $3x + 4y$ is equivalent to $(3)(4) + xy$ because of any order, any grouping. Is he correct? Why or why not?

Relevant Vocabulary

VARIABLE (DESCRIPTION): A *variable* is a symbol (such as a letter) that represents a number (i.e., it is a placeholder for a number).

NUMERICAL EXPRESSION (DESCRIPTION): A *numerical expression* is a number, or it is any combination of sums, differences, products, or divisions of numbers that evaluates to a number.

VALUE OF A NUMERICAL EXPRESSION: The *value of a numerical expression* is the number found by evaluating the expression.

EXPRESSION (DESCRIPTION): An *expression* is a numerical expression, or it is the result of replacing some (or all) of the numbers in a numerical expression with variables.

EQUIVALENT EXPRESSIONS: Two expressions are *equivalent* if both expressions evaluate to the same number for every substitution of numbers into all the letters in both expressions.

AN EXPRESSION IN EXPANDED FORM: An expression that is written as sums (and/or differences) of products whose factors are numbers, variables, or variables raised to whole number powers is said to be in *expanded form*. A single number, variable, or a single product of numbers and/or variables is also considered to be in expanded form. Examples of expressions in expanded form include: $324, 3x, 5x + 3 - 40,$ and $x + 2x + 3x$.

TERM (DESCRIPTION): Each summand of an expression in expanded form is called a *term*. For example, the expression $2x + 3x + 5$ consists of three terms: $2x, 3x,$ and 5.

COEFFICIENT OF THE TERM (DESCRIPTION): The number found by multiplying just the numbers in a term together is the *coefficient of the term*. For example, given the product $2 \cdot x \cdot 4$, its equivalent term is $8x$. The number 8 is called the coefficient of the term $8x$.

AN EXPRESSION IN STANDARD FORM: An expression in expanded form with all its like terms collected is said to be in *standard form*. For example, $2x + 3x + 5$ is an expression written in expanded form; however, to be written in standard form, the like terms $2x$ and $3x$ must be combined. The equivalent expression $5x + 5$ is written in standard form.

Lesson Summary

Terms that contain exactly the same variable symbol can be combined by addition or subtraction because the variable represents the same number. Any order, any grouping can be used where terms are added (or subtracted) in order to group together like terms. Changing the orders of the terms in a sum does not affect the value of the expression for given values of the variable(s).

Problem Set

For Problems 1–9, write equivalent expressions by combining like terms. Verify the equivalence of your expression and the given expression by evaluating each for the given values: $a = 2$, $b = 5$, and $c = -3$.

1. $3a + 5a$

2. $8b - 4b$

3. $5c + 4c + c$

4. $3a + 6 + 5a$

5. $8b + 8 - 4b$

6. $5c - 4c + c$

7. $3a + 6 + 5a - 2$

8. $8b + 8 - 4b - 3$

9. $5c - 4c + c - 3c$

Use any order, any grouping to write equivalent expressions by combining like terms. Then, verify the equivalence of your expression to the given expression by evaluating for the value(s) given in each problem.

10. $3(6a)$; for $a = 3$

11. $5d(4)$; for $d = -2$

12. $(5r)(-2)$; for $r = -3$

13. $3b(8) + (-2)(7c)$; for $b = 2$, $c = 3$

14. $-4(3s) + 2(-t)$; for $s = \frac{1}{2}$, $t = -3$

15. $9(4p) - 2(3q) + p$; for $p = -1$, $q = 4$

16. $7(4g) + 3(5h) + 2(-3g)$; for $g = \frac{1}{2}$, $h = \frac{1}{3}$

© 2015 Great Minds. eureka-math.org
G7-M3M4-SE-B2-1.3.1-02.2016

The problems below are follow-up questions to Example 1, part (b) from Classwork: Find the sum of $2x + 1$ and $5x$.

17. Jack got the expression $7x + 1$ and then wrote his answer as $1 + 7x$. Is his answer an equivalent expression? How do you know?

18. Jill also got the expression $7x + 1$, and then wrote her answer as $1x + 7$. Is her expression an equivalent expression? How do you know?

© 2015 Great Minds. eureka-math.org
G7-M3M4-SE-B2-1.3.1-02.2016

Lesson 2: Generating Equivalent Expressions

Opening Exercise

Additive inverses have a sum of zero. Fill in the center column of the table with the opposite of the given number or expression, then show the proof that they are opposites. The first row is completed for you.

Expression	Opposite	Proof of Opposites
1	-1	$1 + (-1) = 0$
3		
-7		
$-\dfrac{1}{2}$		
x		
$3x$		
$x + 3$		
$3x - 7$		

Example 1: Subtracting Expressions

a. Subtract: $(40 + 9) - (30 + 2)$.

b. Subtract: $(3x + 5y - 4) - (4x + 11)$.

Example 2: Combining Expressions Vertically

a. Find the sum by aligning the expressions vertically.
$(5a + 3b - 6c) + (2a - 4b + 13c)$

b. Find the difference by aligning the expressions vertically.
$(2x + 3y - 4) - (5x + 2)$

EUREKA
MATH

© 2015 Great Minds. eureka-math.org
G7-M3M4-SE-B2-1.3.1-02.2016

Example 3: Using Expressions to Solve Problems

A stick is x meters long. A string is 4 times as long as the stick.

a. Express the length of the string in terms of x.

b. If the total length of the string and the stick is 15 meters long, how long is the string?

Example 4: Expressions from Word Problems

It costs Margo a processing fee of $3 to rent a storage unit, plus $17 per month to keep her belongings in the unit. Her friend Carissa wants to store a box of her belongings in Margo's storage unit and tells her that she will pay her $1 toward the processing fee and $3 for every month that she keeps the box in storage. Write an expression in standard form that represents how much Margo will have to pay for the storage unit if Carissa contributes. Then, determine how much Margo will pay if she uses the storage unit for 6 months.

Example 5: Extending Use of the Inverse to Division

Multiplicative inverses have a product of 1. Find the multiplicative inverses of the terms in the first column. Show that the given number and its multiplicative inverse have a product of 1. Then, use the inverse to write each corresponding expression in standard form. The first row is completed for you.

Given	Multiplicative Inverse	Proof—Show that their product is 1.	Use each inverse to write its corresponding expression below in standard form.
3	$\frac{1}{3}$	$3 \cdot \frac{1}{3}$ $\frac{3}{1} \cdot \frac{1}{3}$ $\frac{3}{3}$ $\frac{1}{1}$	$12 \div 3$ $12 \cdot \frac{1}{3}$ 4
5			$65 \div 5$
-2			$18 \div (-2)$
$-\frac{3}{5}$			$6 \div \left(-\frac{3}{5}\right)$
x			$5x \div x$
$2x$			$12x \div 2x$

EUREKA
MATH

Relevant Vocabulary

AN EXPRESSION IN EXPANDED FORM: An expression that is written as sums (and/or differences) of products whose factors are numbers, variables, or variables raised to whole number powers is said to be in *expanded form*. A single number, variable, or a single product of numbers and/or variables is also considered to be in expanded form. Examples of expressions in expanded form include: 324, $3x$, $5x + 3 - 40$, and $x + 2x + 3x$.

TERM: Each summand of an expression in expanded form is called a *term*. For example, the expression $2x + 3x + 5$ consists of 3 terms: $2x$, $3x$, and 5.

COEFFICIENT OF THE TERM: The number found by multiplying just the numbers in a term together is called the *coefficient*. For example, given the product $2 \cdot x \cdot 4$, its equivalent term is $8x$. The number 8 is called the coefficient of the term $8x$.

AN EXPRESSION IN STANDARD FORM: An expression in expanded form with all of its like terms collected is said to be in *standard form*. For example, $2x + 3x + 5$ is an expression written in expanded form; however, to be written in standard form, the like terms 2x and 3x must be combined. The equivalent expression 5x + 5 is written in standard form.

Lesson Summary

- Rewrite subtraction as adding the opposite before using any order, any grouping.
- Rewrite division as multiplying by the reciprocal before using any order, any grouping.
- The opposite of a sum is the sum of its opposites.
- Division is equivalent to multiplying by the reciprocal.

Problem Set

1. Write each expression in standard form. Verify that your expression is equivalent to the one given by evaluating each expression using $x = 5$.

a. $3x + (2 - 4x)$	b. $3x + (-2 + 4x)$	c. $-3x + (2 + 4x)$
d. $3x + (-2 - 4x)$	e. $3x - (2 + 4x)$	f. $3x - (-2 + 4x)$
g. $3x - (-2 - 4x)$	h. $3x - (2 - 4x)$	i. $-3x - (-2 - 4x)$

   j. In problems (a)–(d) above, what effect does addition have on the terms in parentheses when you removed the parentheses?

   k. In problems (e)–(i), what effect does subtraction have on the terms in parentheses when you removed the parentheses?

2. Write each expression in standard form. Verify that your expression is equivalent to the one given by evaluating each expression for the given value of the variable.

a. $4y - (3 + y)$; $y = 2$	b. $(2b + 1) - b$; $b = -4$	c. $(6c - 4) - (c - 3)$; $c = -7$
d. $(d + 3d) - (-d + 2)$; $d = 3$	e. $(-5x - 4) - (-2 - 5x)$; $x = 3$	f. $11f - (-2f + 2)$; $f = \frac{1}{2}$
g. $-5g + (6g - 4)$; $g = -2$	h. $(8h - 1) - (h + 3)$; $h = -3$	i. $(7 + w) - (w + 7)$; $w = -4$
j. $(2g + 9h - 5) - (6g - 4h + 2)$; $g = -2$ and $h = 5$		

EUREKA MATH™

3. Write each expression in standard form. Verify that your expression is equivalent to the one given by evaluating both expressions for the given value of the variable.

a. $-3(8x)$; $x = \frac{1}{4}$	b. $5 \cdot k \cdot (-7)$; $k = \frac{3}{5}$	c. $2(-6x) \cdot 2$; $x = \frac{3}{4}$
d. $-3(8x) + 6(4x)$; $x = 2$	e. $8(5m) + 2(3m)$; $m = -2$	f. $-6(2v) + 3a(3)$; $v = \frac{1}{3}$; $a = \frac{2}{3}$

4. Write each expression in standard form. Verify that your expression is equivalent to the one given by evaluating both expressions for the given value of the variable.

a. $8x \div 2$; $x = -\frac{1}{4}$	b. $18w \div 6$; $w = 6$	c. $25r \div 5r$; $r = -2$
d. $33y \div 11y$; $y = -2$	e. $56k \div 2k$; $k = 3$	f. $24xy \div 6y$; $x = -2$; $y = 3$

5. For each problem (a)–(g), write an equation in standard form.

    a. Find the sum of $-3x$ and $8x$.

    b. Find the sum of $-7g$ and $4g + 2$.

    c. Find the difference when $6h$ is subtracted from $2h - 4$.

    d. Find the difference when $-3n - 7$ is subtracted from $n + 4$.

    e. Find the result when $13v + 2$ is subtracted from $11 + 5v$.

    f. Find the result when $-18m - 4$ is added to $4m - 14$.

    g. What is the result when $-2x + 9$ is taken away from $-7x + 2$?

6. Marty and Stewart are stuffing envelopes with index cards. They are putting x index cards in each envelope. When they are finished, Marty has 15 stuffed envelopes and 4 extra index cards, and Stewart has 12 stuffed envelopes and 6 extra index cards. Write an expression in standard form that represents the number of index cards the boys started with. Explain what your expression means.

7. The area of the pictured rectangle below is $24b$ ft². Its width is $2b$ ft. Find the height of the rectangle and name any properties used with the appropriate step.

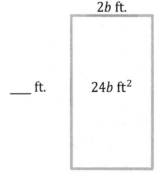

This page intentionally left blank

Lesson 3: Writing Products as Sums and Sums as Products

Opening Exercise

Solve the problem using a tape diagram. A sum of money was shared between George and Benjamin in a ratio of $3:4$. If the sum of money was $56.00, how much did George get?

Represent $3 + 2$ using a tape diagram.

Represent $x + 2$ using a tape diagram.

Draw a rectangular array for $3(3 + 2)$.

Draw an array for $3(x + 2)$.

Key Terms

DISTRIBUTIVE PROPERTY: The *distributive property* can be written as the identity

$$a(b + c) = ab + ac \text{ for all numbers } a, b, \text{ and } c.$$

Exercise 1

Determine the area of each region using the distributive property.

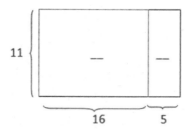

Example 2

Draw a tape diagram to represent each expression.

   a. $(x + y) + (x + y) + (x + y)$

   b. $(x + x + x) + (y + y + y)$

   c. $3x + 3y$

   d. $3(x + y)$

Example 3

Find an equivalent expression by modeling with a rectangular array and applying the distributive property to the expression $5(8x + 3)$.

Exercise 2

For parts (a) and (b), draw an array for each expression and apply the distributive property to expand each expression. Substitute the given numerical values to demonstrate equivalency.

a. $2(x + 1), x = 5$

b. $10(2c + 5), c = 1$

EUREKA
MATH

© 2015 Great Minds. eureka-math.org
G7-M3M4-SE-B2-1.3.1-02.2016

For parts (c) and (d), apply the distributive property. Substitute the given numerical values to demonstrate equivalency.

    c. $3(4f - 1), f = 2$

    d. $9(-3r - 11), r = 10$

Example 4

Rewrite the expression $(6x + 15) \div 3$ in standard form using the distributive property.

Exercise 3

Rewrite the expressions in standard form.

    a. $(2b + 12) \div 2$

    b. $(20r - 8) \div 4$

    c. $(49g - 7) \div 7$

Example 5

Expand the expression $4(x + y + z)$.

Exercise 4

Expand the expression from a product to a sum by removing grouping symbols using an area model and the repeated use of the distributive property: $3(x + 2y + 5z)$.

        Lesson 3:   Writing Products as Sums and Sums as Products

EUREKA MATH™

Example 6

A square fountain area with side length s ft. is bordered by a single row of square tiles as shown. Express the total number of tiles needed in terms of s three different ways.

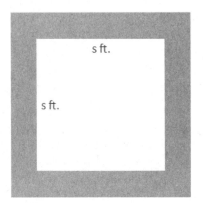

 1 ft.

1 ft.

Problem Set

1.

a. Write two equivalent expressions that represent the rectangular array below.

b. Verify informally that the two expressions are equivalent using substitution.

2. You and your friend made up a basketball shooting game. Every shot made from the free throw line is worth 3 points, and every shot made from the half-court mark is worth 6 points. Write an equation that represents the total number of points, P, if f represents the number of shots made from the free throw line, and h represents the number of shots made from half-court. Explain the equation in words.

3. Use a rectangular array to write the products in standard form.

a. $2(x + 10)$

b. $3(4b + 12c + 11)$

4. Use the distributive property to write the products in standard form.

a. $3(2x - 1)$ g. $(40s + 100t) \div 10$

b. $10(b + 4c)$ h. $(48p + 24) \div 6$

c. $9(g - 5h)$ i. $(2b + 12) \div 2$

d. $7(4n - 5m - 2)$ j. $(20r - 8) \div 4$

e. $a(b + c + 1)$ k. $(49g - 7) \div 7$

f. $(8j - 3l + 9)6$ l. $(14g + 22h) \div \dfrac{1}{2}$

5. Write the expression in standard form by expanding and collecting like terms.

a. $4(8m - 7n) + 6(3n - 4m)$

b. $9(r - s) + 5(2r - 2s)$

c. $12(1 - 3g) + 8(g + f)$

EUREKA
MATH™

© 2015 Great Minds. eureka-math.org
G7-M3M4-SE-B2-1.3.1-02.2016

Lesson 4: Writing Products as Sums and Sums as Products

Classwork

Example 1

a.	$2(x + 5)$	
b.	$3(x + 4)$	
c.	$6(x + 1)$	
d.	$7(x - 3)$	
e.		$5x + 30$
f.		$8x + 8$
g.		$3x - 12$
h.		$15x + 20$

Exercise 1

Rewrite the expressions as a product of two factors.

a. $72t + 8$

b. $55a + 11$

c. $36z + 72$

d. $144q - 15$

e. $3r + 3s$

Example 2

Let the variables x and y stand for positive integers, and let $2x$, $12y$, and 8 represent the area of three regions in the array. Determine the length and width of each rectangle if the width is the same for each rectangle.

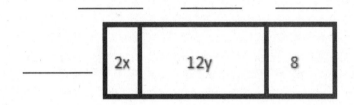

Exercise 2

a.   Write the product and sum of the expressions being represented in the rectangular array.

	12d	4e	3
2	24d	8e	6

b.   Factor $48j + 60k + 24$ by finding the greatest common factor of the terms.

EUREKA
MATH

Exercise 3

For each expression, write each sum as a product of two factors. Emphasize the importance of the distributive property. Use various equivalent expressions to justify equivalency.

a. $2 \cdot 3 + 5 \cdot 3$ b. $(2 + 5) + (2 + 5) + (2 + 5)$ c. $2 \cdot 2 + (5 + 2) + (5 \cdot 2)$

d. $x \cdot 3 + 5 \cdot 3$ e. $(x + 5) + (x + 5) + (x + 5)$ f. $2x + (5 + x) + 5 \cdot 2$

g. $x \cdot 3 + y \cdot 3$ h. $(x + y) + (x + y) + (x + y)$ i. $2x + (y + x) + 2y$

Example 3

A new miniature golf and arcade opened up in town. For convenient ordering, a play package is available to purchase. It includes two rounds of golf and 20 arcade tokens, plus $3.00 off the regular price. There is a group of six friends purchasing this package. Let g represent the cost of a round of golf, and let t represent the cost of a token. Write two different expressions that represent the total amount this group spent. Explain how each expression describes the situation in a different way.

Exercise 4

    a.   What is the opposite of $(-6v + 1)$?

    b.   Using the distributive property, write an equivalent expression for part (a).

Example 5

Rewrite $5a - (a - 3b)$ in standard form. Justify each step, applying the rules for subtracting and the distributive property.

Exercise 5

Expand each expression and collect like terms.

    a. $-3(2p - 3q)$

    b. $-a - (a - b)$

Problem Set

1. Write each expression as the product of two factors.

   a. $1 \cdot 3 + 7 \cdot 3$

   b. $(1 + 7) + (1 + 7) + (1 + 7)$

   c. $2 \cdot 1 + (1 + 7) + (7 \cdot 2)$

   d. $h \cdot 3 + 6 \cdot 3$

   e. $(h + 6) + (h + 6) + (h + 6)$

   f. $2h + (6 + h) + 6 \cdot 2$

   g. $j \cdot 3 + k \cdot 3$

   h. $(j + k) + (j + k) + (j + k)$

   i. $2j + (k + j) + 2k$

2. Write each sum as a product of two factors.

   a. $6 \cdot 7 + 3 \cdot 7$

   b. $(8 + 9) + (8 + 9) + (8 + 9)$

   c. $4 + (12 + 4) + (5 \cdot 4)$

   d. $2y \cdot 3 + 4 \cdot 3$

   e. $(x + 5) + (x + 5)$

   f. $3x + (2 + x) + 5 \cdot 2$

   g. $f \cdot 6 + g \cdot 6$

   h. $(c + d) + (c + d) + (c + d) + (c + d)$

   i. $2r + r + s + 2s$

3. Use the following rectangular array to answer the questions below.

?	?	?	?
?	15f	5g	45

   a.   Fill in the missing information.

   b.   Write the sum represented in the rectangular array.

   c.   Use the missing information from part (a) to write the sum from part (b) as a product of two factors.

4. Write the sum as a product of two factors.

   a. $81w + 48$

   b. $10 - 25t$

   c. $12a + 16b + 8$

5. Xander goes to the movies with his family. Each family member buys a ticket and two boxes of popcorn. If there are five members of his family, let t represent the cost of a ticket and p represent the cost of a box of popcorn. Write two different expressions that represent the total amount his family spent. Explain how each expression describes the situation in a different way.

6. Write each expression in standard form.

    a. $-3(1 - 8m - 2n)$

    b. $5 - 7(-4q + 5)$

    c. $-(2h - 9) - 4h$

    d. $6(-5r - 4) - 2(r - 7s - 3)$

7. Combine like terms to write each expression in standard form.

    a. $(r - s) + (s - r)$

    b. $(-r + s) + (s - r)$

    c. $(-r - s) - (-s - r)$

    d. $(r - s) + (s - t) + (t - r)$

    e. $(r - s) - (s - t) - (t - r)$

© 2015 Great Minds. eureka-math.org
G7-M3M4-SE-B2-1.3.1-02.2016

Lesson 5: Using the Identity and Inverse to Write Equivalent Expressions

Opening Exercise

a. In the morning, Harrison checked the temperature outside to find that it was $-12°F$. Later in the afternoon, the temperature rose $12°F$. Write an expression representing the temperature change. What was the afternoon temperature?

b. Rewrite subtraction as adding the inverse for the following problems and find the sum.

i. $2 - 2$

ii. $-4 - (-4)$

iii. The difference of 5 and 5

iv. $g - g$

c. What pattern do you notice in part (a) and (b)?

d. Add or subtract.

i. $16 + 0$

ii. $0 - 7$

iii. $-4 + 0$

iv. $0 + d$

v. What pattern do you notice in parts (i) through (iv)?

e. Your younger sibling runs up to you and excitedly exclaims, "I'm thinking of a number. If I add it to the number 2 ten times, that is, 2 + my number + my number + my number, and so on, then the answer is 2. What is my number?" You almost immediately answer, "zero," but are you sure? Can you find a different number (other than zero) that has the same property? If not, can you justify that your answer is the only correct answer?

Example 1

Write the sum, and then write an equivalent expression by collecting like terms and removing parentheses.

    a. $2x$ and $-2x + 3$

    b. $2x - 7$ and the opposite of $2x$

    c.   The opposite of $(5x - 1)$ and $5x$

Exercise 1

With a partner, take turns alternating roles as writer and speaker. The speaker verbalizes how to rewrite the sum and properties that justify each step as the writer writes what is being spoken without any input. At the end of each problem, discuss in pairs the resulting equivalent expressions.

Write the sum, and then write an equivalent expression by collecting like terms and removing parentheses whenever possible.

    a. -4 and $4b + 4$

    b. $3x$ and $1 - 3x$

c.   The opposite of $4x$ and $-5 + 4x$

d.   The opposite of $-10t$ and $t - 10t$

e.   The opposite of $(-7 - 4v)$ and $-4v$

Example 2

- $\left(\frac{3}{4}\right) \times \left(\frac{4}{3}\right) =$
- $4 \times \frac{1}{4} =$
- $\frac{1}{9} \times 9 =$
- $\left(-\frac{1}{3}\right) \times -3 =$
- $\left(-\frac{6}{5}\right) \times \left(-\frac{5}{6}\right) =$

Write the product, and then write the expression in standard form by removing parentheses and combining like terms. Justify each step.

a.   The multiplicative inverse of $\frac{1}{5}$ and $\left(2x - \frac{1}{5}\right)$

b.   The multiplicative inverse of 2 and $(2x + 4)$

EUREKA MATH™

© 2015 Great Minds. eureka-math.org
G7-M3M4-SE-B2-1.3.1-02.2016

    c.   The multiplicative inverse of $\left(\dfrac{1}{3x+5}\right)$ and $\dfrac{1}{3}$

Exercise 2

Write the product, and then write the expression in standard form by removing parentheses and combining like terms. Justify each step.

    a.   The reciprocal of 3 and $-6y - 3x$

    b.   The multiplicative inverse of 4 and $4h - 20$

    c.   The multiplicative inverse of $-\dfrac{1}{6}$ and $2 - \dfrac{1}{6}j$

Problem Set

1. Fill in the missing parts.

   a. The sum of $6c - 5$ and the opposite of $6c$

   $(6c - 5) + (-6c)$

   _____   Rewrite subtraction as addition

   $6c + (-6c) + (-5)$ _____

   $0 + (-5)$ _____

   _____   Additive identity property of zero

   b. The product of $-2c + 14$ and the multiplicative inverse of -2

   $(-2c + 14)\left(-\frac{1}{2}\right)$

   $(-2c)\left(-\frac{1}{2}\right) + (14)\left(-\frac{1}{2}\right)$ _____

   _____   Multiplicative inverse, multiplication

   $1c - 7$ Adding the additive inverse is the same as subtraction

   $c - 7$ _____

2. Write the sum, and then rewrite the expression in standard form by removing parentheses and collecting like terms.

   a. 6 and $p - 6$

   b. $10w + 3$ and -3

   c. $-x - 11$ and the opposite of -11

   d. The opposite of $4x$ and $3 + 4x$

   e. $2g$ and the opposite of $(1 - 2g)$

3. Write the product, and then rewrite the expression in standard form by removing parentheses and collecting like terms.

   a. $7h - 1$ and the multiplicative inverse of 7

   b. The multiplicative inverse of -5 and $10v - 5$

   c. $9 - b$ and the multiplicative inverse of 9

   d. The multiplicative inverse of $\frac{1}{4}$ and $5t - \frac{1}{4}$

   e. The multiplicative inverse of $-\frac{1}{10x}$ and $\frac{1}{10x} - \frac{1}{10}$

4. Write the expressions in standard form.

a. $\frac{1}{4}\left(4x + 8\right)$

b. $\frac{1}{6}\left(r - 6\right)$

c. $\frac{4}{5}\left(x + 1\right)$

d. $\frac{1}{8}\left(2x + 4\right)$

e. $\frac{3}{4}\left(5x - 1\right)$

f. $\frac{1}{5}\left(10x - 5\right) - 3$

This page intentionally left blank

Lesson 6: Collecting Rational Number Like Terms

Classwork

Opening Exercise

Solve each problem, leaving your answers in standard form. Show your steps.

a.   Terry weighs 40 kg. Janice weighs $2\frac{3}{4}$ kg less than Terry. What is their combined weight?

b. $2\frac{2}{3} - 1\frac{1}{2} - \frac{4}{5}$

c. $\frac{1}{5} + (-4)$

d. $4\left(\frac{3}{5}\right)$

e.   Mr. Jackson bought $1\frac{3}{5}$ lb. of beef. He cooked $\frac{3}{4}$ of it for lunch. How much does he have left?

Example 1

Rewrite the expression in standard form by collecting like terms.

$$\frac{2}{3}n - \frac{3}{4}n + \frac{1}{6}n + 2\frac{2}{9}n$$

Exercise 1

For the following exercises, predict how many terms the resulting expression will have after collecting like terms. Then, write the expression in standard form by collecting like terms.

a. $\frac{2}{5}g - \frac{1}{6} - g + \frac{3}{10}g - \frac{4}{5}$

b. $i + 6i - \frac{3}{7}i + \frac{1}{3}h + \frac{1}{2}i - h + \frac{1}{4}h$

Example 2

At a store, a shirt was marked down in price by $10.00. A pair of pants doubled in price. Following these changes, the price of every item in the store was cut in half. Write two different expressions that represent the new cost of the items, using s for the cost of each shirt and p for the cost of a pair of pants. Explain the different information each one shows.

EUREKA
MATH™

Exercise 2

Write two different expressions that represent the total cost of the items if tax was $\frac{1}{10}$ of the original price. Explain the different information each shows.

Example 3

Write this expression in standard form by collecting like terms. Justify each step.

$$5\frac{1}{3} - \left(3\frac{1}{3}\right)\left(\frac{1}{2}x - \frac{1}{4}\right)$$

Exercise 3

Rewrite the following expressions in standard form by finding the product and collecting like terms.

a. $-6\frac{1}{3} - \frac{1}{2}\left(\frac{1}{2} + y\right)$

b. $\frac{2}{3} + \frac{1}{3}\left(\frac{1}{4}f - 1\frac{1}{3}\right)$

Example 4

Model how to write the expression in standard form using rules of rational numbers.

$$\frac{x}{20} + \frac{2x}{5} + \frac{x+1}{2} + \frac{3x-1}{10}$$

EUREKA
MATH™

Evaluate the original expression and the answers when $x = 20$. Do you get the same number?

Exercise 4

Rewrite the following expression in standard form by finding common denominators and collecting like terms.

$$\frac{2h}{3} - \frac{h}{9} + \frac{h-4}{6}$$

Example 5

Rewrite the following expression in standard form.

$$\frac{2(3x-4)}{6} - \frac{5x+2}{8}$$

Method 1:	Method 2a:	Method 2b:	Method 3:

Exercise 5

Write the following expression in standard form.

$$\frac{2x-11}{4} - \frac{3(x-2)}{10}$$

EUREKA
MATH™

Problem Set

1. Write the indicated expressions.

   a. $\frac{1}{2}m$ inches in feet.

   b. The perimeter of a square with $\frac{2}{3}g$ cm sides.

   c. The number of pounds in 9 oz.

   d. The average speed of a train that travels x miles in $\frac{3}{4}$ hour.

   e. Devin is $1\frac{1}{4}$ years younger than Eli. April is $\frac{1}{5}$ as old as Devin. Jill is 5 years older than April. If Eli is E years old, what is Jill's age in terms of E?

2. Rewrite the expressions by collecting like terms.

   a. $\frac{1}{2}k - \frac{3}{8}k$

   b. $\frac{2r}{5} + \frac{7r}{15}$

   c. $-\frac{1}{3}a - \frac{1}{2}b - \frac{3}{4} + \frac{1}{2}b - \frac{2}{3}b + \frac{5}{6}a$

   d. $-p + \frac{3}{5}q - \frac{1}{10}q + \frac{1}{9} - \frac{1}{9}p + 2\frac{1}{3}p$

   e. $\frac{5}{7}y - \frac{y}{14}$

   f. $\frac{3n}{8} - \frac{n}{4} + 2\frac{n}{2}$

3. Rewrite the expressions by using the distributive property and collecting like terms.

   a. $\frac{4}{5}(15x - 5)$

   b. $\frac{4}{5}\left(\frac{1}{4}c - 5\right)$

   c. $2\frac{4}{5}v - \frac{2}{3}\left(4v + 1\frac{1}{6}\right)$

   d. $8 - 4\left(\frac{1}{8}r - 3\frac{1}{2}\right)$

   e. $\frac{1}{7}(14x + 7) - 5$

   f. $\frac{1}{5}(5x - 15) - 2x$

   g. $\frac{1}{4}(p + 4) + \frac{3}{5}(p - 1)$

   h. $\frac{7}{8}(w + 1) + \frac{5}{6}(w - 3)$

   i. $\frac{4}{5}(c - 1) - \frac{1}{8}(2c + 1)$

   j. $\frac{2}{3}\left(h + \frac{3}{4}\right) - \frac{1}{3}\left(h + \frac{3}{4}\right)$

   k. $\frac{2}{3}\left(h + \frac{3}{4}\right) - \frac{2}{3}\left(h - \frac{3}{4}\right)$

   l. $\frac{2}{3}\left(h + \frac{3}{4}\right) + \frac{2}{3}\left(h - \frac{3}{4}\right)$

   m. $\frac{k}{2} - \frac{4k}{5} - 3$

   n. $\frac{3t + 2}{7} + \frac{t - 4}{14}$

   o. $\frac{9x - 4}{10} + \frac{3x + 2}{5}$

   p. $\frac{3(5g - 1)}{4} - \frac{2g + 7}{6}$

   q. $-\frac{3d + 1}{5} + \frac{d - 5}{2} + \frac{7}{10}$

   r. $\frac{9w}{6} + \frac{2w - 7}{3} - \frac{w - 5}{4}$

   s. $\frac{1 + f}{5} - \frac{1 + f}{3} + \frac{3 - f}{6}$

This page intentionally left blank

Lesson 7: Understanding Equations

Opening Exercise

Your brother is going away to college, so you no longer have to share a bedroom. You decide to redecorate a wall by hanging two new posters on the wall. The wall is 14 feet wide and each poster is four feet wide. You want to place the posters on the wall so that the distance from the edge of each poster to the nearest edge of the wall is the same as the distance between the posters, as shown in the diagram below. Determine that distance.

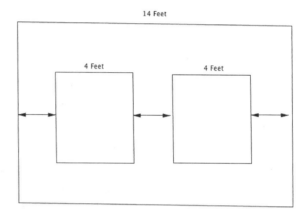

Your parents are redecorating the dining room and want to place two rectangular wall sconce lights that are 25 inches wide along a $10\frac{2}{3}$-foot wall so that the distance between the lights and the distances from each light to the nearest edge of the wall are all the same. Design the wall and determine the distance.

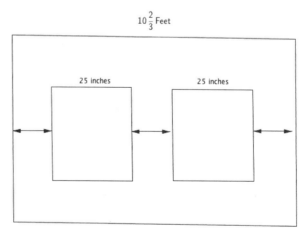

Let the distance between a light and the nearest edge of a wall be x ft. Write an expression in terms of x for the total length of the wall. Then, use the expression and the length of the wall given in the problem to write an equation that can be used to find that distance.

Now write an equation where y stands for the number of *inches*: Let the distance between a light and the nearest edge of a wall be y inches. Write an expression in terms of y for the total length of the wall. Then, use the expression and the length of the wall to write an equation that can be used to find that distance (in inches).

What value(s) of y makes the second equation true: 24, 25, or 26?

Example

The ages of three sisters are consecutive integers. The sum of their ages is 45. Calculate their ages.

   a.   Use a tape diagram to find their ages.

   b.   If the youngest sister is x years old, describe the ages of the other two sisters in terms of x, write an expression for the sum of their ages in terms of x, and use that expression to write an equation that can be used to find their ages.

   c.   Determine if your answer from part (a) is a solution to the equation you wrote in part (b).

© 2015 Great Minds. eureka-math.org
G7-M3M4-SE-B2-1.3.1-02.2016

Exercise

Sophia pays a $19.99 membership fee for an online music store.

a. If she also buys two songs from a new album at a price of $0.99 each, what is the total cost?

b. If Sophia purchases n songs for $0.99 each, write an expression for the total cost.

c. Sophia's friend has saved $118 but is not sure how many songs she can afford if she buys the membership and some songs. Use the expression in part (b) to write an equation that can be used to determine how many songs Sophia's friend can buy.

d. Using the equation written in part (c), can Sophia's friend buy 101, 100, or 99 songs?

Relevant Vocabulary

VARIABLE (DESCRIPTION): A *variable* is a symbol (such as a letter) that represents a number (i.e., it is a placeholder for a number).

EQUATION: An *equation* is a statement of equality between two expressions.

NUMBER SENTENCE: A *number sentence* is a statement of equality between two numerical expressions.

SOLUTION: A *solution* to an equation with one variable is a number that, when substituted for the variable in both expressions, makes the equation a true number sentence.

Lesson Summary

In many word problems, an equation is often formed by setting an expression equal to a number. To build the expression, it is helpful to consider a few numerical calculations with just numbers first. For example, if a pound of apples costs \$2, then three pounds cost \$6 (2×3), four pounds cost \$8 (2×4), and n pounds cost $2n$ dollars. If we had \$15 to spend on apples and wanted to know how many pounds we could buy, we can use the expression $2n$ to write an equation, $2n = 15$, which can then be used to find the answer: $7\frac{1}{2}$ pounds.

To determine if a number is a solution to an equation, substitute the number into the equation for the variable (letter) and check to see if the resulting number sentence is true. If it is true, then the number is a solution to the equation. For example, $7\frac{1}{2}$ is a solution to $2n = 15$ because $2\left(7\frac{1}{2}\right) = 15$.

Problem Set

1. Check whether the given value is a solution to the equation.

   a. $4n - 3 = -2n + 9$ $n = 2$

   b. $9m - 19 = 3m + 1$ $m = \dfrac{10}{3}$

   c. $3(y + 8) = 2y - 6$ $y = 30$

2. Tell whether each number is a solution to the problem modeled by the following equation.

   Mystery Number: Five more than -8 times a number is 29. What is the number?

   Let the mystery number be represented by n.
   The equation is $5 + (-8)n = 29$.

   a. Is 3 a solution to the equation? Why or why not?

   b. Is -4 a solution to the equation? Why or why not?

   c. Is -3 a solution to the equation? Why or why not?

   d. What is the mystery number?

3. The sum of three consecutive integers is 36.

   a. Find the smallest integer using a tape diagram.

   b. Let n represent the smallest integer. Write an equation that can be used to find the smallest integer.

   c. Determine if each value of n below is a solution to the equation in part (b).

   $n = 12.5$

   $n = 12$

   $n = 11$

4. Andrew is trying to create a number puzzle for his younger sister to solve. He challenges his sister to find the mystery number. "When 4 is subtracted from half of a number the result is 5." The equation to represent the mystery number is $\frac{1}{2}m - 4 = 5$. Andrew's sister tries to guess the mystery number.

   a. Her first guess is 30. Is she correct? Why or why not?

   b. Her second guess is 2. Is she correct? Why or why not?

   c. Her final guess is $4\frac{1}{2}$. Is she correct? Why or why not?

Lesson 8: Using If-Then Moves in Solving Equations

Opening Exercise

Recall and summarize the if-then moves.

Write $3 + 5 = 8$ in as many true equations as you can using the if-then moves. Identify which if-then move you used.

Example 1

Julia, Keller, and Israel are volunteer firefighters. On Saturday, the volunteer fire department held its annual coin drop fundraiser at a streetlight. After one hour, Keller had collected $42.50 more than Julia, and Israel had collected $15 less than Keller. The three firefighters collected $125.95 in total. How much did each person collect?

Find the solution using a tape diagram.

© 2015 Great Minds. eureka-math.org
G7-M3M4-SE-B2-1.3.1-02.2016

What were the operations we used to get our answer?

The amount of money Julia collected is j dollars. Write an expression to represent the amount of money Keller collected in dollars.

Using the expressions for Julia and Keller, write an expression to represent the amount of money Israel collected in dollars.

Using the expressions written above, write an equation in terms of j that can be used to find the amount each person collected.

Solve the equation written above to determine the amount of money each person collected and describe any if-then moves used.

EUREKA
MATH™

© 2015 Great Minds. eureka-math.org
G7-M3M4-SE-B2-1.3.1-02.2016

Example 2

You are designing a rectangular pet pen for your new baby puppy. You have 30 feet of fence barrier. You decide that you would like the length to be $6\frac{1}{3}$ feet longer than the width.

Draw and label a diagram to represent the pet pen. Write expressions to represent the width and length of the pet pen.

Find the dimensions of the pet pen.

Example 3

Nancy's morning routine involves getting dressed, eating breakfast, making her bed, and driving to work. Nancy spends $\frac{1}{3}$ of the total time in the morning getting dressed, 10 minutes eating breakfast, 5 minutes making her bed and the remaining time driving to work. If Nancy spent $35\frac{1}{2}$ minutes getting dressed, eating breakfast, and making her bed, how long was her drive to work?

Write and solve this problem using an equation. Identify the if-then moves used when solving the equation.

Is your answer reasonable? Explain.

© 2015 Great Minds. eureka-math.org
G7-M3M4-SE-B2-1.3.1-02.2016

Example 4

The total number of participants who went on the seventh-grade field trip to the Natural Science Museum consisted of all of the seventh-grade students and 7 adult chaperones. Two-thirds of the total participants rode a large bus, and the rest rode a smaller bus. If 54 people rode the large bus, how many students went on the field trip?

© 2015 Great Minds. eureka-math.org
G7-M3M4-SE-B2-1.3.1-02.2016

Lesson Summary

Algebraic Approach: To *solve an equation* algebraically means to use the properties of operations and if-then moves to simplify the equation into a form where the solution is easily recognizable. For the equations we are studying this year (called linear equations), that form is an equation that looks like $x = a\ number$, where the number is the solution.

If-Then Moves: If x is a solution to an equation, it will continue to be a solution to the new equation formed by adding or subtracting a number from both sides of the equation. It will also continue to be a solution when both sides of the equation are multiplied by or divided by a nonzero number. We use these if-then moves to make zeros and ones in ways that simplify the original equation.

Useful First Step: If one is faced with the task of finding a solution to an equation, a useful first step is to collect like terms on each side of the equation.

Problem Set

Write and solve an equation for each problem.

1. The perimeter of a rectangle is 30 inches. If its length is three times its width, find the dimensions.

2. A cell phone company has a basic monthly plan of $40 plus $0.45 for any minutes used over 700. Before receiving his statement, John saw he was charged a total of $48.10. Write and solve an equation to determine how many minutes he must have used during the month. Write an equation without decimals.

3. A volleyball coach plans her daily practices to include 10 minutes of stretching, $\frac{2}{3}$ of the entire practice scrimmaging, and the remaining practice time working on drills of specific skills. On Wednesday, the coach planned 100 minutes of stretching and scrimmaging. How long, in hours, is the entire practice?

4. The sum of two consecutive even numbers is 54. Find the numbers.

5. Justin has $7.50 more than Eva, and Emma has $12 less than Justin. Together, they have a total of $63.00. How much money does each person have?

6. Barry's mountain bike weighs 6 pounds more than Andy's. If their bikes weigh 42 pounds altogether, how much does Barry's bike weigh? Identify the if-then moves in your solution.

7. Trevor and Marissa together have 26 T-shirts to sell. If Marissa has 6 fewer T-shirts than Trevor, find how many T-shirts Trevor has. Identify the if-then moves in your solution.

© 2015 Great Minds. eureka-math.org
G7-M3M4-SE-B2-1.3.1-02.2016

8. A number is $\frac{1}{7}$ of another number. The difference of the numbers is 18. (Assume that you are subtracting the smaller number from the larger number.) Find the numbers.

9. A number is 6 greater than $\frac{1}{2}$ another number. If the sum of the numbers is 21, find the numbers.

10. Kevin is currently twice as old now as his brother. If Kevin was 8 years old 2 years ago, how old is Kevin's brother now?

11. The sum of two consecutive odd numbers is 156. What are the numbers?

12. If n represents an odd integer, write expressions in terms of n that represent the next three consecutive odd integers. If the four consecutive odd integers have a sum of 56, find the numbers.

13. The cost of admission to a history museum is \$3.25 per person over the age of 3; kids 3 and under get in for free. If the total cost of admission for the Warrick family, including their two 6-month old twins, is \$19.50, find how many family members are over 3 years old.

14. Six times the sum of three consecutive odd integers is -18. Find the integers.

15. I am thinking of a number. If you multiply my number by 4, add -4 to the product, and then take $\frac{1}{3}$ of the sum, the result is -6. Find my number.

16. A vending machine has twice as many quarters in it as dollar bills. If the quarters and dollar bills have a combined value of \$96.00, how many quarters are in the machine?

This page intentionally left blank

Lesson 9: Using If-Then Moves in Solving Equations

Opening Exercise

Heather practices soccer and piano. Each day she practices piano for 2 hours. After 5 days, she practiced both piano and soccer for a total of 20 hours. Assuming that she practiced soccer the same amount of time each day, how many hours per day, h, did Heather practice soccer?

Over 5 days, Jake practices piano for a total of 2 hours. Jake practices soccer for the same amount of time each day. If he practiced piano and soccer for a total of 20 hours, how many hours, h, per day did Jake practice soccer?

Example 1

Fred and Sam are a team in the local 138.2 mile bike-run-athon. Fred will compete in the bike race, and Sam will compete in the run. Fred bikes at an average speed of 8 miles per hour and Sam runs at an average speed of 4 miles per hour. The bike race begins at 6:00 a.m., followed by the run. Sam predicts he will finish the run at 2:33 a.m. the next morning.

    a.   How many hours will it take them to complete the entire bike-run-athon?

    b.   If t is how long it takes Fred to complete the bike race, in hours, write an expression to find Fred's total distance.

    c.   Write an expression, in terms of t to express Sam's time.

    d.   Write an expression, in terms of t, that represents Sam's total distance.

    e.   Write and solve an equation using the total distance both Fred and Sam will travel.

f.   How far will Fred bike, and how much time will it take him to complete his leg of the race?

g.   How far will Sam run, and how much time will it take him to complete his leg of the race?

Total Time (hours)	Fred's Time (hours)	Sam's Time (hours)
10	6	
15	12	
20	8	
18.35	8	
20.55	t	

Example 2

Shelby is seven times as old as Bonnie. If in 5 years, the sum of Bonnie and Shelby's ages is 98, find Bonnie's present age. Use an algebraic approach.

Problem Set

1. A company buys a digital scanner for \$12,000. The value of the scanner is $12{,}000\left(1 - \dfrac{n}{5}\right)$ after n years. The company has budgeted to replace the scanner when the trade-in value is \$2,400. After how many years should the company plan to replace the machine in order to receive this trade-in value?

2. Michael is 17 years older than John. In 4 years, the sum of their ages will be 49. Find Michael's present age.

3. Brady rode his bike 70 miles in 4 hours. He rode at an average speed of 17 mph for t hours and at an average rate of speed of 22 mph for the rest of the time. How long did Brady ride at the slower speed? Use the variable t to represent the time, in hours, Brady rode at 17 mph.

4. Caitlan went to the store to buy school clothes. She had a store credit from a previous return in the amount of \$39.58. If she bought 4 of the same style shirt in different colors and spent a total of \$52.22 after the store credit was taken off her total, what was the price of each shirt she bought? Write and solve an equation with integer coefficients.

5. A young boy is growing at a rate of 3.5 cm per month. He is currently 90 cm tall. At that rate, in how many months will the boy grow to a height of 132 cm?

6. The sum of a number, $\dfrac{1}{6}$ of that number, $2\dfrac{1}{2}$ of that number, and 7 is $12\dfrac{1}{2}$. Find the number.

7. The sum of two numbers is 33 and their difference is 2. Find the numbers.

8. Aiden refills three token machines in an arcade. He puts twice the number of tokens in machine A as in machine B, and in machine C, he puts $\dfrac{3}{4}$ what he put in machine A. The three machines took a total of 18,324 tokens. How many did each machine take?

9. Paulie ordered 250 pens and 250 pencils to sell for a theatre club fundraiser. The pens cost 11 cents more than the pencils. If Paulie's total order costs \$42.50, find the cost of each pen and pencil.

10. A family left their house in two cars at the same time. One car traveled an average of 7 miles per hour faster than the other. When the first car arrived at the destination after $5\dfrac{1}{2}$ hours of driving, both cars had driven a total of 599.5 miles. If the second car continues at the same average speed, how much time, to the nearest minute, will it take before the second car arrives?

11. Emily counts the triangles and parallelograms in an art piece and determines that altogether, there are 42 triangles and parallelograms. If there are 150 total sides, how many triangles and parallelograms are there?

12. Stefan is three years younger than his sister Katie. The sum of Stefan's age 3 years ago and $\dfrac{2}{3}$ of Katie's age at that time is 12. How old is Katie now?

13. Lucas bought a certain weight of oats for his horse at a unit price of \$0.20 per pound. The total cost of the oats left him with \$1. He wanted to buy the same weight of enriched oats instead, but at \$0.30 per pound, he would have been \$2 short of the total amount due. How much money did Lucas have to buy oats?

© 2015 Great Minds. eureka-math.org
G7-M3M4-SE-B2-1.3.1-02.2016

Lesson 10: Angle Problems and Solving Equations

Classwork

Angle Facts and Definitions

Name of Angle Relationship	Angle Fact	Diagram
Adjacent Angles		
Vertical Angles (vert. ∠s)		
Angles on a Line (∠s on a line)		
Angles at a Point (∠s at a point)		

Opening Exercise

Use the diagram to complete the chart.

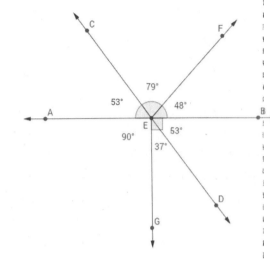

Name the angles that are ...	
Vertical	
Adjacent	
Angles on a line	
Angles at a point	

Example 1

Estimate the measurement of x. _____

In a complete sentence, describe the angle relationship in the diagram.

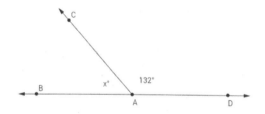

Write an equation for the angle relationship shown in the figure and solve for x. Then, find the measures of $\angle BAC$ and confirm your answers by measuring the angle with a protractor.

EUREKA
MATH™

© 2015 Great Minds. eureka-math.org
G7-M3M4-SE-B2-1.3.1-02.2016

Exercise 1

In a complete sentence, describe the angle relationship in the diagram.

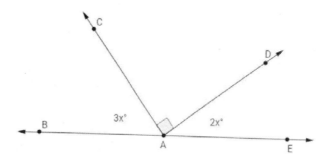

Find the measurements of $\angle BAC$ and $\angle DAE$.

Example 2

In a complete sentence, describe the angle relationship in the
diagram.

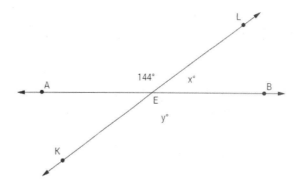

Write an equation for the angle relationship shown in the figure and solve for x and y. Find the measurements of $\angle LEB$ and $\angle KEB$.

Exercise 2

In a complete sentence, describe the angle relationships in the diagram.

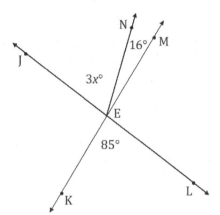

Write an equation for the angle relationship shown in the figure and solve for x.

Example 3

In a complete sentence, describe the angle relationships in the diagram.

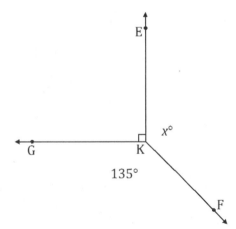

Write an equation for the angle relationship shown in the figure and solve for x. Find the measurement of $\angle EKF$ and confirm your answers by measuring the angle with a protractor.

EUREKA
MATH™

Exercise 3

In a complete sentence, describe the angle relationships in the diagram.

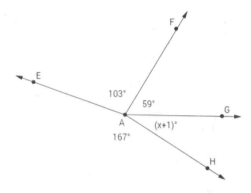

Find the measurement of ∠GAH.

Example 4

The following two lines intersect. The ratio of the measurements of the obtuse angle to the acute angle in any adjacent angle pair in this figure is $2 : 1$. In a complete sentence, describe the angle relationships in the diagram.

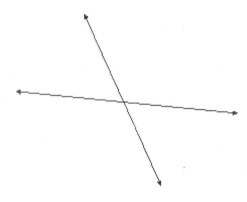

Label the diagram with expressions that describe this relationship. Write an equation that models the angle relationship and solve for x. Find the measurements of the acute and obtuse angles.

Exercise 4

The ratio of $m\angle GFH$ to $m\angle EFH$ is $2 : 3$. In a complete sentence, describe the angle relationships in the diagram.

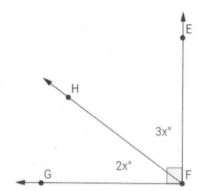

Find the measures of $\angle GFH$ and $\angle EFH$.

Relevant Vocabulary

ADJACENT ANGLES: Two angles $\angle BAC$ and $\angle CAD$ with a common side $\overrightarrow{AC}$ are *adjacent angles* if C belongs to the interior of $\angle BAD$.

VERTICAL ANGLES: Two angles are *vertical angles* (or *vertically opposite angles)* if their sides form two pairs of opposite rays.

ANGLES ON A LINE: The sum of the measures of adjacent *angles on a line* is $180°$.

ANGLES AT A POINT: The sum of the measures of adjacent *angles at a point* is $360°$.

© 2015 Great Minds. eureka-math.org
G7-M3M4-SE-B2-1.3.1-02.2016

Problem Set

For each question, use angle relationships to write an equation in order to solve for each variable. Determine the indicated angles. You can check your answers by measuring each angle with a protractor.

1. In a complete sentence, describe the relevant angle relationships in the following diagram. Find the measurement of $\angle DAE$.

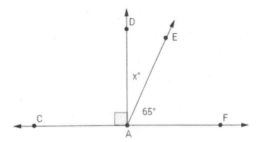

2. In a complete sentence, describe the relevant angle relationships in the following diagram. Find the measurement of $\angle QPR$.

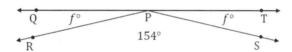

3. In a complete sentence, describe the relevant angle relationships in the following diagram. Find the measurements of $\angle CQD$ and $\angle EQF$.

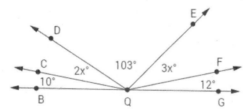

4. In a complete sentence, describe the relevant angle relationships in the following diagram. Find the measure of x.

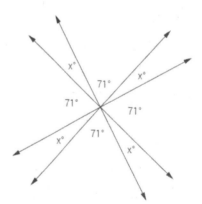

5. In a complete sentence, describe the relevant angle relationships in the following diagram. Find the measures of x and y.

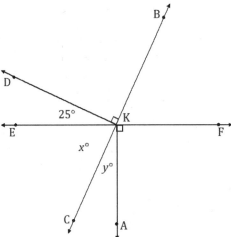

6. In a complete sentence, describe the relevant angle relationships in the following diagram. Find the measures of x and y.

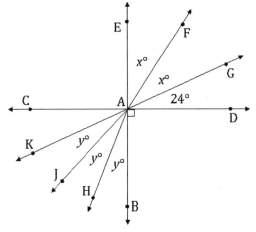

7. In a complete sentence, describe the relevant angle relationships in the following diagram. Find the measures of $\angle CAD$ and $\angle DAE$.

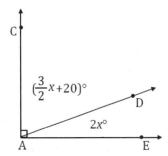

EUREKA
MATH™

8. In a complete sentence, describe the relevant angle relationships in the following diagram. Find the measure of $\angle CQG$.

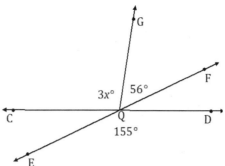

9. The ratio of the measures of a pair of adjacent angles on a line is $4 : 5$.

   a. Find the measures of the two angles.

   b. Draw a diagram to scale of these adjacent angles. Indicate the measurements of each angle.

10. The ratio of the measures of three adjacent angles on a line is $3 : 4 : 5$.

   a. Find the measures of the three angles.

   b. Draw a diagram to scale of these adjacent angles. Indicate the measurements of each angle.

This page intentionally left blank

Lesson 11: Angle Problems and Solving Equations

Opening Exercise

a.   In a complete sentence, describe the angle relationship in the diagram. Write an equation for the angle relationship shown in the figure and solve for x. Confirm your answer by measuring the angle with a protractor.

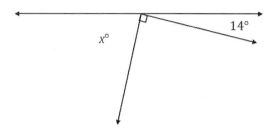

b. $\overleftrightarrow{CD}$ and $\overleftrightarrow{EF}$ are intersecting lines. In a complete sentence, describe the angle relationship in the diagram. Write an equation for the angle relationship shown in the figure and solve for y. Confirm your answer by measuring the angle with a protractor.

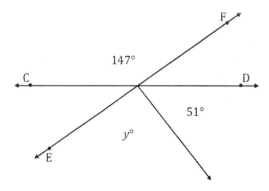

c. In a complete sentence, describe the angle relationship in the diagram. Write an equation for the angle relationship shown in the figure and solve for b. Confirm your answer by measuring the angle with a protractor.

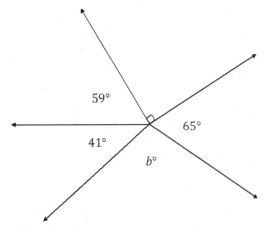

d. The following figure shows three lines intersecting at a point. In a complete sentence, describe the angle relationship in the diagram. Write an equation for the angle relationship shown in the figure and solve for z. Confirm your answer by measuring the angle with a protractor.

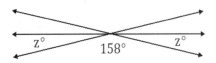

e. Write an equation for the angle relationship shown in the figure and solve for x. In a complete sentence, describe the angle relationship in the diagram. Find the measurements of $\angle EPB$ and $\angle CPA$. Confirm your answers by measuring the angles with a protractor.

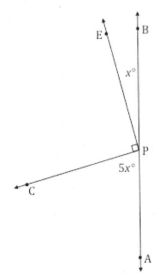

© 2015 Great Minds. eureka-math.org
G7-M3M4-SE-B2-1.3.1-02.2016

EUREKA MATH™

Example 1

The following figure shows three lines intersecting at a point. In a complete sentence, describe the angle relationship in the diagram. Write an equation for the angle relationship shown in the figure and solve for x. Confirm your answer by measuring the angle with a protractor.

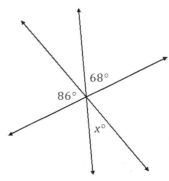

Exercise 1

The following figure shows four lines intersecting at a point. In a complete sentence, describe the angle relationships in the diagram. Write an equation for the angle relationship shown in the figure and solve for x and y. Confirm your answers by measuring the angles with a protractor.

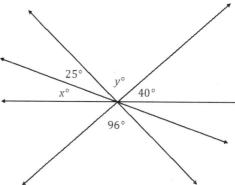

Example 2

In a complete sentence, describe the angle relationships in the diagram. You may label the diagram to help describe the angle relationships. Write an equation for the angle relationship shown in the figure and solve for x. Confirm your answer by measuring the angle with a protractor.

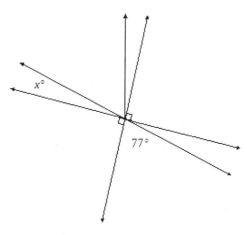

Exercise 2

In a complete sentence, describe the angle relationships in the diagram. Write an equation for the angle relationship shown in the figure and solve for x and y. Confirm your answers by measuring the angles with a protractor.

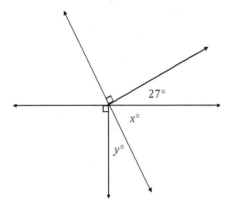

Example 3

In a complete sentence, describe the angle relationships in the diagram. Write an equation for the angle relationship shown in the figure and solve for x. Find the measures of $\angle JAH$ and $\angle GAF$. Confirm your answers by measuring the angles with a protractor.

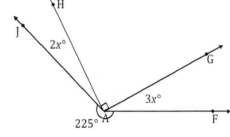

Exercise 3

In a complete sentence, describe the angle relationships in the diagram. Write an equation for the angle relationship shown in the figure and solve for x. Find the measure of $\angle JKG$. Confirm your answer by measuring the angle with a protractor.

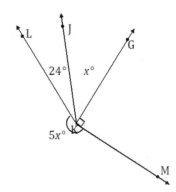

EUREKA MATH™

© 2015 Great Minds. eureka-math.org
G7-M3M4-SE-B2-1.3.1-02.2016

Example 4

In the accompanying diagram, the measure of ∠DBE is four times the measure of ∠FBG.

a. Label ∠DBE as $y°$ and ∠FBG as $x°$. Write an equation that
    describes the relationship between ∠DBE and ∠FBG.

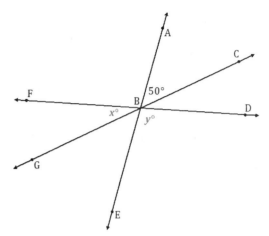

b. Find the value of x.

c. Find the measures of ∠FBG, ∠CBD, ∠ABF, ∠GBE, and ∠DBE.

d. What is the measure of ∠ABG? Identify the angle relationship used to get your answer.

Problem Set

In a complete sentence, describe the angle relationships in each diagram. Write an equation for the angle relationship(s) shown in the figure, and solve for the indicated unknown angle. You can check your answers by measuring each angle with a protractor.

1. Find the measures of ∠EAF, ∠DAE, and ∠CAD.

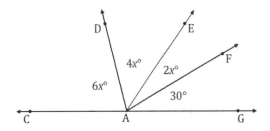

2. Find the measure of a.

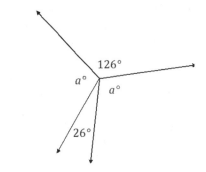

3. Find the measures of x and y.

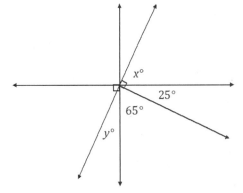

EUREKA
MATH™

© 2015 Great Minds. eureka-math.org
G7-M3M4-SE-B2-1.3.1-02.2016

4. Find the measure of ∠HAJ.

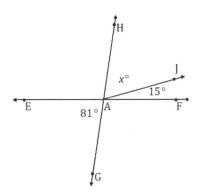

5. Find the measures of ∠HAB and ∠CAB.

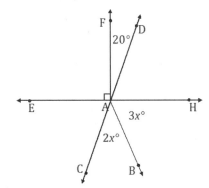

6. The measure of ∠SPT is $b°$. The measure of ∠TPR is five more than two times ∠SPT. The measure of ∠QPS is twelve less than eight times the measure of ∠SPT. Find the measures of ∠SPT, ∠TPR, and ∠QPS.

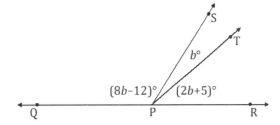

7.   Find the measures of $\angle HQE$ and $\angle AQG$.

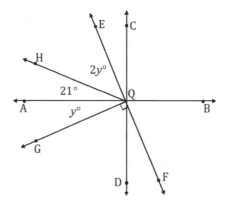

8.   The measures of three angles at a point are in the ratio of $2:3:5$. Find the measures of the angles.

9.   The sum of the measures of two adjacent angles is $72°$. The ratio of the smaller angle to the larger angle is $1:3$. Find the measure of each angle.

10. Find the measures of $\angle CQA$ and $\angle EQB$.

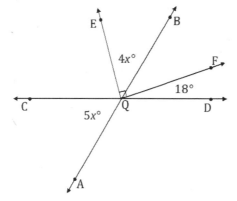

EUREKA
MATH™

© 2015 Great Minds. eureka-math.org
G7-M3M4-SE-B2-1.3.1-02.2016

Lesson 12: Properties of Inequalities

Example 1

Preserves the inequality symbol:

Reverses the inequality symbol:

Station 1

Die 1	Inequality	Die 2	Operation	New Inequality	Inequality Symbol Preserved or Reversed?
-3	$<$	5	Add 2	$-3 + 2 < 5 + 2$ $-1 < 7$	Preserved
			Add -3		
			Subtract 2		
			Subtract -1		
			Add 1		

Examine the results. Make a statement about what you notice, and justify it with evidence.

© 2015 Great Minds. eureka-math.org
G7-M3M4-SE-B2-1.3.1-02.2016

Station 2

Die 1	Inequality	Die 2	Operation	New Inequality	Inequality Symbol Preserved or Reversed?
-3	$<$	4	Multiply by -1	$(-1)(-3) < (-1)(4)$ $3 > -4$	Reversed
			Multiply by -1		
			Multiply by -1		
			Multiply by -1		
			Multiply by -1		

Examine the results. Make a statement about what you notice and justify it with evidence.

Lesson 12:   Properties of Inequalities

EUREKA
MATH™

© 2015 Great Minds. eureka-math.org
G7-M3M4-SE-B2-1.3.1-02.2016

Station 3

Die 1	Inequality	Die 2	Operation	New Inequality	Inequality Symbol Preserved or Reversed?
-2	$>$	-4	Multiply by $\dfrac{1}{2}$	$(-2)\left(\dfrac{1}{2}\right) > (-4)\left(\dfrac{1}{2}\right)$ $-1 > -2$	Preserved
			Multiply by 2		
			Divide by 2		
			Divide by $\dfrac{1}{2}$		
			Multiply by 3		

Examine the results. Make a statement about what you notice, and justify it with evidence.

© 2015 Great Minds. eureka-math.org
G7-M3M4-SE-B2-1.3.1-02.2016

Station 4

Die 1	Inequality	Die 2	Operation	New Inequality	Inequality Symbol Preserved or Reversed?
3	$>$	-2	Multiply by -2	$3(-2) > (-2)(-2)$ $-6 < 4$	Reversed
			Multiply by -3		
			Divide by -2		
			Divide by $-\dfrac{1}{2}$		
			Multiply by $-\dfrac{1}{2}$		

Examine the results. Make a statement about what you notice and justify it with evidence.

Lesson 12:   Properties of Inequalities

EUREKA MATH™

© 2015 Great Minds. eureka-math.org
G7-M3M4-SE-B2-1.3.1-02.2016

Exercise

Complete the following chart using the given inequality, and determine an operation in which the inequality symbol is preserved and an operation in which the inequality symbol is reversed. Explain why this occurs.

Inequality	Operation and New Inequality Which Preserves the Inequality Symbol	Operation and New Inequality Which Reverses the Inequality Symbol	Explanation
$2 < 5$			
$-4 > -6$			
$-1 \leq 2$			
$-2 + (-3) < -3 - 1$			

Lesson Summary

When both sides of an inequality are added or subtracted by a number, the inequality symbol stays the same, and the inequality symbol is said to be _____.

When both sides of an inequality are multiplied or divided by a positive number, the inequality symbol stays the same, and the inequality symbol is said to be _____.

When both sides of an inequality are multiplied or divided by a negative number, the inequality symbol switches from $<$ to $>$ or from $>$ to $<$. The inequality symbol is _____.

Problem Set

1. For each problem, use the properties of inequalities to write a true inequality statement. The two integers are -2 and -5.

   a. Write a true inequality statement.

   b. Subtract -2 from each side of the inequality. Write a true inequality statement.

   c. Multiply each number by -3. Write a true inequality statement.

2. On a recent vacation to the Caribbean, Kay and Tony wanted to explore the ocean elements. One day they went in a submarine 150 feet below sea level. The second day they went scuba diving 75 feet below sea level.

   a. Write an inequality comparing the submarine's elevation and the scuba diving elevation.

   b. If they only were able to go one-fifth of the capable elevations, write a new inequality to show the elevations they actually achieved.

   c. Was the inequality symbol preserved or reversed? Explain.

3. If a is a negative integer, then which of the number sentences below is true? If the number sentence is not true, give a reason.

   a. $5 + a < 5$

   b. $5 + a > 5$

   c. $5 - a > 5$

   d. $5 - a < 5$

   e. $5a < 5$

   f. $5a > 5$

   g. $5 + a > a$

   h. $5 + a < a$

   i. $5 - a > a$

   j. $5 - a < a$

   k. $5a > a$

   l. $5a < a$

Lesson 12:   Properties of Inequalities   **EUREKA MATH**

© 2015 Great Minds. eureka-math.org
G7-M3M4-SE-B2-1.3.1-02.2016

Lesson 13: Inequalities

Opening Exercise: Writing Inequality Statements

Tarik is trying to save $265.49 to buy a new tablet. Right now, he has $40 and can save $38 a week from his allowance.

Write and evaluate an expression to represent the amount of money saved after …

2 weeks

3 weeks

4 weeks

5 weeks

6 weeks

7 weeks

8 weeks

When will Tarik have enough money to buy the tablet?

Write an inequality that will generalize the problem.

Example 1: Evaluating Inequalities—Finding a Solution

The sum of two consecutive odd integers is more than −12. Write several true numerical inequality expressions.

The sum of two consecutive odd integers is more than −12. What is the smallest value that will make this true?

    a.   Write an inequality that can be used to find the smallest value that will make the statement true.

EUREKA
MATH™

© 2015 Great Minds. eureka-math.org
G7-M3M4-SE-B2-1.3.1-02.2016

b. Use if-then moves to solve the inequality written in part (a). Identify where the 0's and 1's were made using the if-then moves.

c. What is the smallest value that will make this true?

Exercises

1. Connor went to the county fair with $22.50 in his pocket. He bought a hot dog and drink for $3.75 and then wanted to spend the rest of his money on ride tickets, which cost $1.25 each.

   a. Write an inequality to represent the total spent where r is the number of tickets purchased.

   b. Connor wants to use this inequality to determine whether he can purchase 10 tickets. Use substitution to show whether he will have enough money.

c.   What is the total maximum number of tickets he can buy based upon the given information?

2.   Write and solve an inequality statement to represent the following problem:

On a particular airline, checked bags can weigh no more than 50 pounds. Sally packed 32 pounds of clothes and five identical gifts in a suitcase that weighs 8 pounds. Write an inequality to represent this situation.

EUREKA
MATH

Problem Set

1. Match each problem to the inequality that models it. One choice will be used twice.

    _____ The sum of three times a number and -4 is greater than 17.   a. $3x + -4 \geq 17$

    _____ The sum of three times a number and -4 is less than 17.   b. $3x + -4 < 17$

    _____ The sum of three times a number and -4 is at most 17.   c. $3x + -4 > 17$

    _____ The sum of three times a number and -4 is no more than 17.   d. $3x + -4 \leq 17$

    _____ The sum of three times a number and -4 is at least 17.

2. If x represents a positive integer, find the solutions to the following inequalities.

    a. $x < 7$ f. $-x \geq 2$

    b. $x - 15 < 20$ g. $\dfrac{x}{3} < 2$

    c. $x + 3 \leq 15$

    d. $-x > 2$ h. $-\dfrac{x}{3} > 2$

    e. $10 - x > 2$ i. $3 - \dfrac{x}{4} > 2$

3. Recall that the symbol $\neq$ means *not equal to*. If x represents a positive integer, state whether each of the following statements is always true, sometimes true, or false.

    a. $x > 0$ e. $x \geq 1$

    b. $x < 0$ f. $x \neq 0$

    c. $x > -5$ g. $x \neq -1$

    d. $x > 1$ h. $x \neq 5$

4. Twice the smaller of two consecutive integers increased by the larger integer is at least 25.

    Model the problem with an inequality, and determine which of the given values 7, 8, and/or 9 are solutions. Then, find the smallest number that will make the inequality true.

5.

    a.   The length of a rectangular fenced enclosure is 12 feet more than the width. If Farmer Dan has 100 feet of fencing, write an inequality to find the dimensions of the rectangle with the largest perimeter that can be created using 100 feet of fencing.

    b.   What are the dimensions of the rectangle with the largest perimeter? What is the area enclosed by this rectangle

6. At most, Kyle can spend $50 on sandwiches and chips for a picnic. He already bought chips for $6 and will buy sandwiches that cost $4.50 each. Write and solve an inequality to show how many sandwiches he can buy. Show your work and interpret your solution.

EUREKA MATH

This page intentionally left blank

Lesson 14: Solving Inequalities

Opening Exercise

The annual County Carnival is being held this summer and will last $5\frac{1}{2}$ days. Use this information and the other given information to answer each problem.

You are the owner of the biggest and newest roller coaster called the Gentle Giant. The roller coaster costs $6 to ride. The operator of the ride must pay $200 per day for the ride rental and $65 per day for a safety inspection. If you want to make a profit of at least $1,000 each day, what is the minimum number of people that must ride the roller coaster?

Write an inequality that can be used to find the minimum number of people, p, which must ride the roller coaster each day to make the daily profit.

Solve the inequality.

Interpret the solution.

Example 1

A youth summer camp has budgeted $2,000 for the campers to attend the carnival. The cost for each camper is $17.95, which includes general admission to the carnival and two meals. The youth summer camp must also pay $250 for the chaperones to attend the carnival and $350 for transportation to and from the carnival. What is the greatest number of campers who can attend the carnival if the camp must stay within its budgeted amount?

Example 2

The carnival owner pays the owner of an exotic animal exhibit $650 for the entire time the exhibit is displayed. The owner of the exhibit has no other expenses except for a daily insurance cost. If the owner of the animal exhibit wants to make more than $500 in profits for the $5\frac{1}{2}$ days, what is the greatest daily insurance rate he can afford to pay?

Example 3

Several vendors at the carnival sell products and advertise their businesses. Shane works for a recreational company that sells ATVs, dirt bikes, snowmobiles, and motorcycles. His boss paid him $500 for working all of the days at the carnival plus 5% commission on all of the sales made at the carnival. What was the minimum amount of sales Shane needed to make if he earned more than $1,500?

Lesson Summary

The key to solving inequalities is to use if-then moves to make 0's and 1's to get the inequality into the form $x > c$ or $x < c$ where c is a number. Adding or subtracting opposites will make 0's. According to the if-then move, any number that is added to or subtracted from each side of an inequality does not change the solution to the inequality. Multiplying and dividing numbers makes 1's. When each side of an inequality is multiplied by or divided by a positive number, the sign of the inequality is not reversed. However, when each side of an inequality is multiplied by or divided by a negative number, the sign of the inequality is reversed.

Given inequalities containing decimals, equivalent inequalities can be created which have only integer coefficients and constant terms by repeatedly multiplying every term by ten until all coefficients and constant terms are integers.

Given inequalities containing fractions, equivalent inequalities can be created which have only integer coefficients and constant terms by multiplying every term by the least common multiple of the values in the denominators.

Problem Set

1. As a salesperson, Jonathan is paid $50 per week plus 3% of the total amount he sells. This week, he wants to earn at least $100. Write an inequality with integer coefficients for the total sales needed to earn at least $100, and describe what the solution represents.

2. Systolic blood pressure is the higher number in a blood pressure reading. It is measured as the heart muscle contracts. Heather was with her grandfather when he had his blood pressure checked. The nurse told him that the upper limit of his systolic blood pressure is equal to half his age increased by 110.

    a. a is the age in years, and p is the systolic blood pressure in millimeters of mercury (mmHg). Write an inequality to represent this situation.

    b. Heather's grandfather is 76 years old. What is *normal* for his systolic blood pressure?

3. Traci collects donations for a dance marathon. One group of sponsors will donate a total of $6 for each hour she dances. Another group of sponsors will donate $75 no matter how long she dances. What number of hours, to the nearest minute, should Traci dance if she wants to raise at least $1,000?

4. Jack's age is three years more than twice the age of his younger brother, Jimmy. If the sum of their ages is at most 18, find the greatest age that Jimmy could be.

5. Brenda has $500 in her bank account. Every week she withdraws $40 for miscellaneous expenses. How many weeks can she withdraw the money if she wants to maintain a balance of a least $200?

6. A scooter travels 10 miles per hour faster than an electric bicycle. The scooter traveled for 3 hours, and the bicycle traveled for $5\frac{1}{2}$ hours. Altogether, the scooter and bicycle traveled no more than 285 miles. Find the maximum speed of each.

Lesson 14:   Solving Inequalities

S.95

This page intentionally left blank

Lesson 15: Graphing Solutions to Inequalities

Exercise 1

1. Two identical cars need to fit into a small garage. The opening is 23 feet 6 inches wide, and there must be at least 3 feet 6 inches of clearance between the cars and between the edges of the garage. How wide can the cars be?

Example

A local car dealership is trying to sell all of the cars that are on the lot. Currently, there are 525 cars on the lot, and the general manager estimates that they will consistently sell 50 cars per week. Estimate how many weeks it will take for the number of cars on the lot to be less than 75.

Write an inequality that can be used to find the number of full weeks, w, it will take for the number of cars to be less than 75. Since w is the number of full or complete weeks, $w = 1$ means at the end of week 1.

Solve and graph the inequality.

Interpret the solution in the context of the problem.

Verify the solution.

Exercise 2

2. The cost of renting a car is $25 per day plus a one-time fee of $75.50 for insurance. How many days can the car be rented if the total cost is to be no more than $525?

    a. Write an inequality to model the situation.

    b. Solve and graph the inequality.

    c. Interpret the solution in the context of the problem.

EUREKA
MATH™

Additional Exercises

For each problem, write, solve, and graph the inequality, and interpret the solution within the context of the problem.

3. Mrs. Smith decides to buy three sweaters and a pair of jeans. She has $120 in her wallet. If the price of the jeans is $35, what is the highest possible price of a sweater, if each sweater is the same price?

4. The members of the Select Chorus agree to buy at least 250 tickets for an outside concert. They buy 20 fewer lawn tickets than balcony tickets. What is the least number of balcony tickets bought?

© 2015 Great Minds. eureka-math.org
G7-M3M4-SE-B2-1.3.1-02.2016

5. Samuel needs $29 to download some songs and movies on his MP3 player. His mother agrees to pay him $6 an hour for raking leaves in addition to his $5 weekly allowance. What is the minimum number of hours Samuel must work in one week to have enough money to purchase the songs and movies?

Problem Set

1. Ben has agreed to play fewer video games and spend more time studying. He has agreed to play less than 10 hours of video games each week. On Monday through Thursday, he plays video games for a total of $5\frac{1}{2}$ hours. For the remaining 3 days, he plays video games for the same amount of time each day. Find t, the amount of time he plays video games, for each of the 3 days. Graph your solution.

2. Gary's contract states that he must work more than 20 hours per week. The graph below represents the number of hours he can work in a week.

    a. Write an algebraic inequality that represents the number of hours, h, Gary can work in a week.

    b. Gary is paid $15.50 per hour in addition to a weekly salary of $50. This week he wants to earn more than $400. Write an inequality to represent this situation.

    c. Solve and graph the solution from part (b). Round to the nearest hour.

3. Sally's bank account has $650 in it. Every week, Sally withdraws $50 to pay for her dog sitter. What is the maximum number of weeks that Sally can withdraw the money so there is at least $75 remaining in the account? Write and solve an inequality to find the solution, and graph the solution on a number line.

4. On a cruise ship, there are two options for an Internet connection. The first option is a fee of $5 plus an additional $0.25 per minute. The second option costs $50 for an unlimited number of minutes. For how many minutes, m, is the first option cheaper than the second option? Graph the solution.

5. The length of a rectangle is 100 centimeters, and its perimeter is greater than 400 centimeters. Henry writes an inequality and graphs the solution below to find the width of the rectangle. Is he correct? If yes, write and solve the inequality to represent the problem and graph. If no, explain the error(s) Henry made.

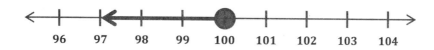

This page intentionally left blank

Lesson 16: The Most Famous Ratio of All

Classwork

Opening Exercise

a.   Using a compass, draw a circle like the picture to the right.

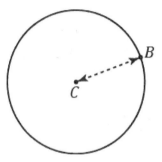

C is the *center* of the circle.
The distance between C and B is the *radius* of the circle.

b.   Write your own definition for the term *circle*.

c.   Extend segment CB to a segment AB in part (a), where A is also a point on the circle.

The length of the segment AB is called the diameter of the circle.

d.   The diameter is _____ as long as the radius.

© 2015 Great Minds. eureka-math.org
G7-M3M4-SE-B2-1.3.1-02.2016

e. Measure the radius and diameter of each circle. The center of each circle is labeled C.

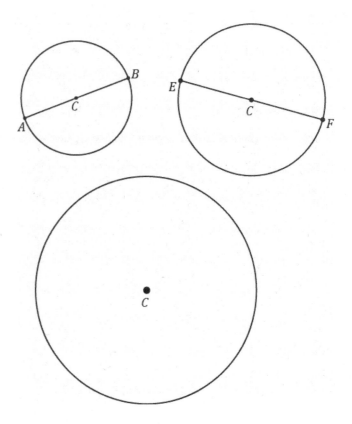

f. Draw a circle of radius 6 cm.

EUREKA
MATH™

© 2015 Great Minds. eureka-math.org
G7-M3M4-SE-B2-1.3.1-02.2016

Mathematical Modeling Exercise

The ratio of the circumference to its diameter is always the same for any circle. The value of this ratio, $\frac{\text{Circumference}}{\text{Diameter}}$, is called the number *pi* and is represented by the symbol π.

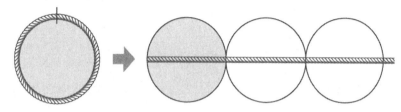

Since the circumference is a little greater than 3 times the diameter, π is a number that is a little greater than 3. Use the symbol π to represent this special number. Pi is a non-terminating, non-repeating decimal, and mathematicians use the symbol π or approximate representations as more convenient ways to represent pi.

- $\pi \approx 3.14$ or $\frac{22}{7}$.

- The ratios of the circumference to the diameter and $\pi : 1$ are equal.

- Circumference of a Circle $= \pi \times$ Diameter.

Example

a. The following circles are not drawn to scale. Find the circumference of each circle. (Use $\frac{22}{7}$ as an approximation for π.)

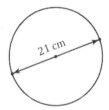
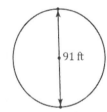
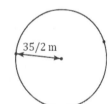

b. The radius of a paper plate is 11.7 cm. Find the circumference to the nearest tenth. (Use 3.14 as an approximation for π.)

© 2015 Great Minds. eureka-math.org
G7-M3M4-SE-B2-1.3.1-02.2016

c. The radius of a paper plate is 11.7 cm. Find the circumference to the nearest hundredth. (Use the π button on your calculator as an approximation for π.)

d. A circle has a radius of r cm and a circumference of C cm. Write a formula that expresses the value of C in terms of r and π.

e. The figure below is in the shape of a semicircle. A semicircle is an arc that is half of a circle. Find the perimeter of the shape. (Use 3.14 for π.)

8 m

Relevant Vocabulary

CIRCLE: Given a point O in the plane and a number $r > 0$, the *circle with center O and radius r* is the set of all points in the plane whose distance from the point O is equal to r.

RADIUS OF A CIRCLE: The *radius* is the length of any segment whose endpoints are the center of a circle and a point that lies on the circle.

DIAMETER OF A CIRCLE: The *diameter of a circle* is the length of any segment that passes through the center of a circle whose endpoints lie on the circle. If r is the *radius* of a circle, then the diameter is $2r$.

The word *diameter* can also mean the segment itself. Context determines how the term is being used: *The diameter* usually refers to the length of the segment, while *a diameter* usually refers to a segment. Similarly, *a radius* can refer to a segment from the center of a circle to a point on the circle.

Circle C

Radii: $\overline{OA}$, $\overline{OB}$, $\overline{OX}$

Diameter: $\overline{AB}$

Circumference

CIRCUMFERENCE: The circumference of a circle is the distance around a circle.

PI: The number *pi*, denoted by π, is the value of the ratio given by the circumference to the diameter, that is $\pi = \dfrac{\text{circumference}}{\text{diameter}}$. The most commonly used approximations for π is 3.14 or $\dfrac{22}{7}$.

SEMICIRCLE: Let C be a circle with center O, and let A and B be the endpoints of a diameter. A *semicircle* is the set containing A, B, and all points that lie in a given half-plane determined by $\overline{AB}$ (diameter) that lie on circle C.

Semicircle

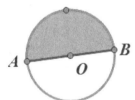

Problem Set

1. Find the circumference.

   a. Give an exact answer in terms of π.

   b. Use $\pi \approx \dfrac{22}{7}$ and express your answer as a fraction in lowest terms.

   c. Use *the* π button on your calculator, and express your answer to the nearest hundredth.

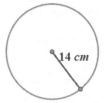

2. Find the circumference.

   a. Give an exact answer in terms of π.

   b. Use $\pi \approx \dfrac{22}{7}$, and express your answer as a fraction in lowest terms.

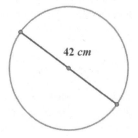

3. The figure shows a circle within a square. Find the circumference of the circle. Let $\pi \approx 3.14$.

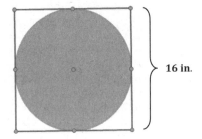

4. Consider the diagram of a semicircle shown.

   a. Explain in words how to determine the perimeter of a semicircle.

   b. Using d to represent the diameter of the circle, write an algebraic equation that will result in the perimeter of a semicircle.

   c. Write another algebraic equation to represent the perimeter of a semicircle using r to represent the radius of a semicircle.

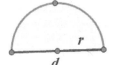

5. Find the perimeter of the semicircle. Let $\pi \approx 3.14$.

EUREKA
MATH™

6. Ken's landscape gardening business makes odd-shaped lawns that include semicircles. Find the length of the edging material needed to border the two lawn designs. Use 3.14 for π.

   a. The radius of this flower bed is 2.5 m.

   b. The diameter of the semicircular section is 10 m, and the lengths of the sides of the two sides are 6 m.

   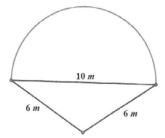

7. Mary and Margaret are looking at a map of a running path in a local park. Which is the shorter path from E to F, along the two semicircles or along the larger semicircle? If one path is shorter, how much shorter is it? Let $\pi \approx 3.14$.

8. Alex the electrician needs 34 yards of electrical wire to complete a job. He has a coil of wiring in his workshop. The coiled wire is 18 inches in diameter and is made up of 21 circles of wire. Will this coil be enough to complete the job? Let $\pi \approx 3.14$.

   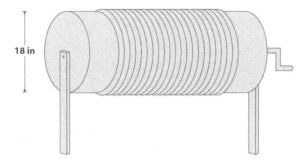

This page intentionally left blank

Lesson 17: The Area of a Circle

Classwork

Exercises 1–3

Solve the problem below individually. Explain your solution.

1. Find the radius a circle if its circumference is 37.68 inches. Use $\pi \approx 3.14$.

2. Determine the area of the rectangle below. Name two ways that can be used to find the area of the rectangle.

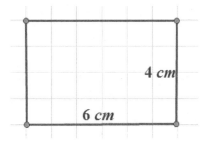

3. Find the length of a rectangle if the area is 27 cm² and the width is 3 cm.

Exploratory Challenge

To find the formula for the area of a circle, cut a circle into 16 equal pieces.

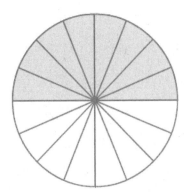

Arrange the triangular wedges by alternating the "triangle" directions and sliding them together to make a "parallelogram." Cut the triangle on the left side in half on the given line, and slide the outside half of the triangle to the other end of the parallelogram in order to create an approximate "rectangle."

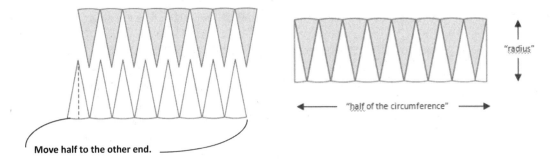

The circumference is $2\pi r$, where the radius is r. Therefore, half of the circumference is πr.

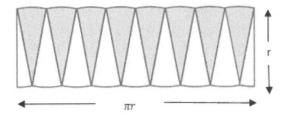

What is the area of the "rectangle" using the side lengths above?

Are the areas of the "rectangle" and the circle the same?

© 2015 Great Minds. eureka-math.org
G7-M3M4-SE-B2-1.3.1-02.2016

EUREKA MATH

If the area of the rectangular shape and the circle are the same, what is the area of the circle?

Example 1

Use the shaded square centimeter units to approximate the area of the circle.

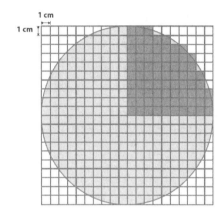

What is the radius of the circle?

What would be a quicker method for determining the area of the circle other than counting all of the squares in the entire circle?

Using the diagram, how many squares were used to cover one-fourth of the circle?

What is the area of the entire circle?

Example 2

A sprinkler rotates in a circular pattern and sprays water over a distance of 12 feet. What is the area of the circular region covered by the sprinkler? Express your answer to the nearest square foot.

Draw a diagram to assist you in solving the problem. What does the distance of 12 feet represent in this problem?

What information is needed to solve the problem?

Example 3

Suzanne is making a circular table out of a square piece of wood. The radius of the circle that she is cutting is 3 feet. How much waste will she have for this project? Express your answer to the nearest square foot.

Draw a diagram to assist you in solving the problem. What does the distance of 3 feet represent in this problem?

What information is needed to solve the problem?

What information do we need to determine the area of the square and the circle?

How will we determine the waste?

Does your solution answer the problem as stated?

Exercises 4–6

4. A circle has a radius of 2 cm.

    a.   Find the exact area of the circular region.

    b.   Find the approximate area using 3.14 to approximate π.

5. A circle has a radius of 7 cm.

    a.   Find the exact area of the circular region.

b.   Find the approximate area using $\frac{22}{7}$ to approximate π.

c.   What is the circumference of the circle?

6.   Joan determined that the area of the circle below is 400π cm^2. Melinda says that Joan's solution is incorrect; she believes that the area is 100π cm^2. Who is correct and why?

20 cm

Relevant Vocabulary

CIRCULAR REGION (OR DISK): Given a point C in the plane and a number $r > 0$, the *circular region (or disk) with center C and radius r* is the set of all points in the plane whose distance from the point C is less than or equal to r.

The boundary of a disk is a circle. The *area of a circle* refers to the area of the disk defined by the circle.

EUREKA
MATH™

© 2015 Great Minds. eureka-math.org
G7-M3M4-SE-B2-1.3.1-02.2016

Problem Set

1. The following circles are not drawn to scale. Find the area of each circle. (Use $\frac{22}{7}$ as an approximation for π.)

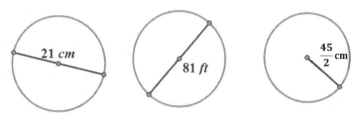

2. A circle has a diameter of 20 inches.
    a. Find the exact area, and find an approximate area using $\pi \approx 3.14$.
    b. What is the circumference of the circle using $\pi \approx 3.14$?

3. A circle has a diameter of 11 inches.
    a. Find the exact area and an approximate area using $\pi \approx 3.14$.
    b. What is the circumference of the circle using $\pi \approx 3.14$?

4. Using the figure below, find the area of the circle.

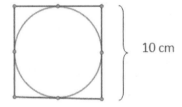

10 cm

5. A path bounds a circular lawn at a park. If the inner edge of the path is 132 ft. around, approximate the amount of area of the lawn inside the circular path. Use $\pi \approx \frac{22}{7}$.

6. The area of a circle is 36π cm^2. Find its circumference.

7. Find the ratio of the area of two circles with radii 3 cm and 4 cm.

8. If one circle has a diameter of 10 cm and a second circle has a diameter of 20 cm, what is the ratio of the area of the larger circle to the area of the smaller circle?

9. Describe a rectangle whose perimeter is 132 ft. and whose area is less than 1 ft^2. Is it possible to find a circle whose circumference is 132 ft. and whose area is less than 1 ft^2? If not, provide an example or write a sentence explaining why no such circle exists.

10. If the diameter of a circle is double the diameter of a second circle, what is the ratio of area of the first circle to the area of the second?

This page intentionally left blank

Lesson 18: More Problems on Area and Circumference

Opening Exercise

Draw a circle with a diameter of 12 cm and a square with a side length of 12 cm on grid paper. Determine the area of the square and the circle.

Brainstorm some methods for finding half the area of the square and half the area of the circle.

Find the area of half of the square and half of the circle, and explain to a partner how you arrived at the area.

What is the ratio of the new area to the original area for the square and for the circle?

Find the area of one-fourth of the square and one-fourth of the circle, first by folding and then by another method. What is the ratio of the new area to the original area for the square and for the circle?

Write an algebraic expression that expresses the area of a semicircle and the area of a quarter circle.

© 2015 Great Minds. eureka-math.org
G7-M3M4-SE-B2-1.3.1-02.2016

Example 1

Find the area of the following semicircle. Use $\pi \approx \frac{22}{7}$.

14 cm

What is the area of the quarter circle? Use $\pi \approx \frac{22}{7}$.

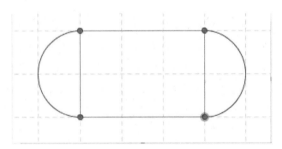

r = 6 cm

Example 2

Marjorie is designing a new set of placemats for her dining room table. She sketched a drawing of the placement on graph paper. The diagram represents the area of the placemat consisting of a rectangle and two semicircles at either end. Each square on the grid measures 4 inches in length.

Find the area of the entire placemat. Explain your thinking regarding the solution to this problem.

If Marjorie wants to make six placemats, how many square inches of fabric will she need? Assume there is no waste.

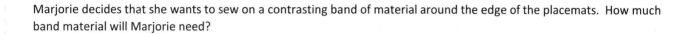

Marjorie decides that she wants to sew on a contrasting band of material around the edge of the placemats. How much band material will Marjorie need?

Example 3

The circumference of a circle is 24π cm. What is the exact area of the circle?

Draw a diagram to assist you in solving the problem.

What information is needed to solve the problem?

Next, find the area.

Exercises

1. Find the area of a circle with a diameter of 42 cm. Use $\pi \approx \frac{22}{7}$.

2. The circumference of a circle is 9π cm.
    a. What is the diameter?

    b. What is the radius?

    c. What is the area?

3. If students only know the radius of a circle, what other measures could they determine? Explain how students would use the radius to find the other parts.

© 2015 Great Minds. eureka-math.org
G7-M3M4-SE-B2-1.3.1-02.2016

EUREKA
MATH™

4. Find the area in the rectangle between the two quarter circles if $AF = 7$ ft, $FB = 9$ ft, and $HD = 7$ ft. Use $\pi \approx \frac{22}{7}$. Each quarter circle in the top-left and lower-right corners have the same radius.

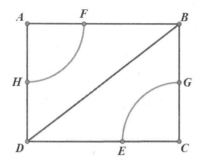

Problem Set

1. Mark created a flower bed that is semicircular in shape, as shown in the image. The diameter of the flower bed is 5 m.

   a. What is the perimeter of the flower bed? (Approximate π to be 3.14.)

   b. What is the area of the flower bed? (Approximate π to be 3.14.)

2. A landscape designer wants to include a semicircular patio at the end of a square sandbox. She knows that the area of the semicircular patio is 25.12 cm^2.

   a. Draw a picture to represent this situation.

   b. What is the length of the side of the square?

3. A window manufacturer designed a set of windows for the top of a two-story wall. If the window is comprised of 2 squares and 2 quarter circles on each end, and if the length of the span of windows across the bottom is 12 feet, approximately how much glass will be needed to complete the set of windows?

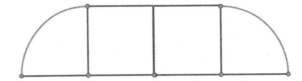

4. Find the area of the shaded region. (Approximate π to be $\frac{22}{7}$.)

5. The figure below shows a circle inside of a square. If the radius of the circle is 8 cm, find the following and explain your solution.

   a. The circumference of the circle

   b. The area of the circle

   c. The area of the square

EUREKA
MATH™

6. Michael wants to create a tile pattern out of three quarter circles for his kitchen backsplash. He will repeat the three quarter circles throughout the pattern. Find the area of the tile pattern that Michael will use. Approximate π as 3.14.

7. A machine shop has a square metal plate with sides that measure 4 cm each. A machinist must cut four semicircles, with a radius of $\frac{1}{2}$ cm and four quarter circles with a radius of 1 cm from its sides and corners. What is the area of the plate formed? Use $\frac{22}{7}$ to approximate π.

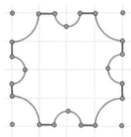

8. A graphic artist is designing a company logo with two concentric circles (two circles that share the same center but have different radii). The artist needs to know the area of the shaded band between the two concentric circles. Explain to the artist how he would go about finding the area of the shaded region.

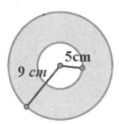

9. Create your own shape made up of rectangles, squares, circles, or semicircles, and determine the area and perimeter.

This page intentionally left blank

Lesson 19: Unknown Area Problems on the Coordinate Plane

Classwork

Example: Area of a Parallelogram

The coordinate plane below contains figure P, parallelogram $ABCD$.

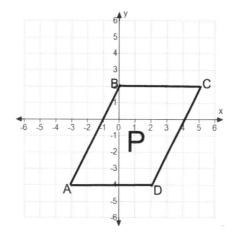

a.   Write the ordered pairs of each of the vertices next to the vertex points.

b.   Draw a rectangle surrounding figure P that has vertex points of A and C. Label the two triangles in the figure as S and T.

c.   Find the area of the rectangle.

d.   Find the area of each triangle.

e.   Use these areas to find the area of parallelogram $ABCD$.

The coordinate plane below contains figure R, a rectangle with the same base as the parallelogram above.

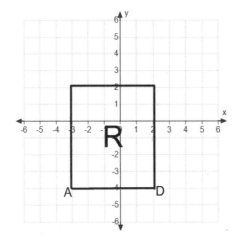

f.   Draw triangles S and T and connect to figure R so that you create a rectangle that is the same size as the rectangle you created on the first coordinate plane.

g.   Find the area of rectangle R.

h.   What do figures R and P have in common?

Exercises

1. Find the area of triangle ABC.

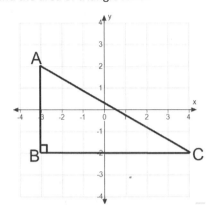

2. Find the area of quadrilateral $ABCD$ two different ways.

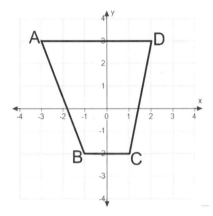

3. The area of quadrilateral $ABCD$ is 12 sq. units. Find x.

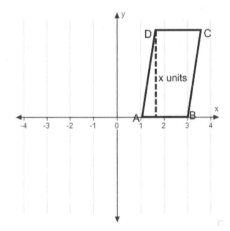

4.   The area of triangle ABC is 14 sq. units. Find the length of side $\overline{BC}$.

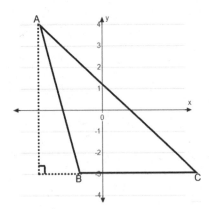

5.   Find the area of triangle ABC.

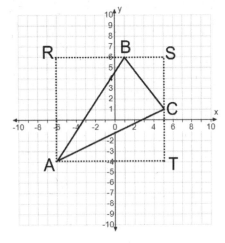

EUREKA
MATH™

© 2015 Great Minds. eureka-math.org
G7-M3M4-SE-B2-1.3.1-02.2016

Problem Set

Find the area of each figure.

1.
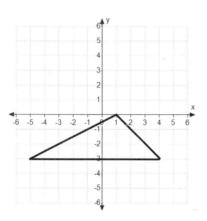

2.
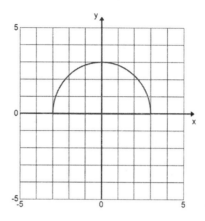

3.
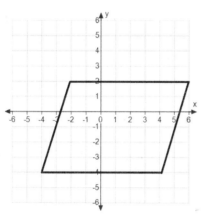

4.
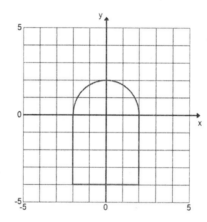

5.
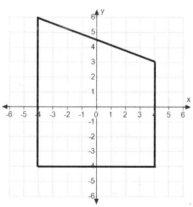

6.
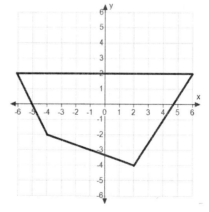

For Problems 7–9, draw a figure in the coordinate plane that matches each description.

7. A rectangle with an area of 18 sq. units

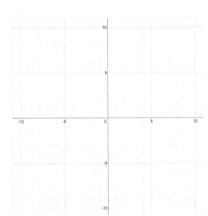

8. A parallelogram with an area of 50 sq. units

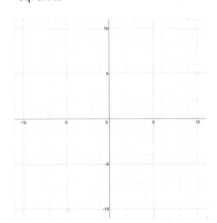

9. A triangle with an area of 25 sq. units

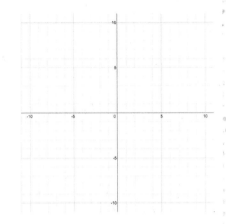

Find the unknown value labelled as x on each figure.

10. The rectangle has an area of 80 sq. units.

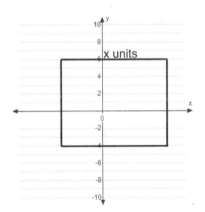

11. The trapezoid has an area of 115 sq. units.

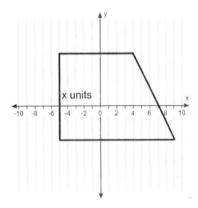

EUREKA
MATH™

12. Find the area of triangle ABC.

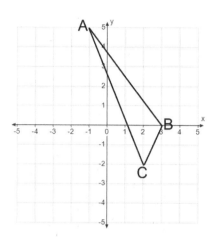

13. Find the area of the quadrilateral using two different methods. Describe the methods used, and explain why they result in the same area.

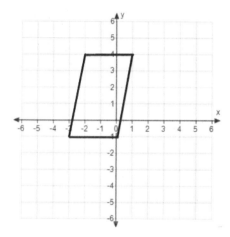

14. Find the area of the quadrilateral using two different methods. What are the advantages or disadvantages of each method?

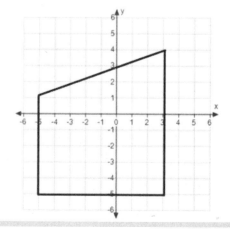

This page intentionally left blank

Lesson 20: Composite Area Problems

Example 1

Find the composite area of the shaded region. Use 3.14 for π.

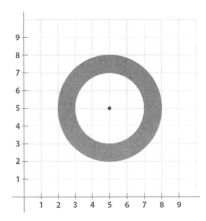

Exercise 1

A yard is shown with the shaded section indicating grassy areas and the unshaded sections indicating paved areas. Find the area of the space covered with grass in units^2.

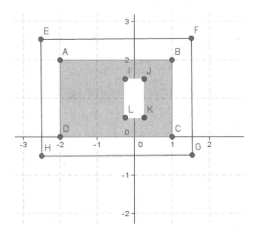

© 2015 Great Minds. eureka-math.org
G7-M3M4-SE-B2-1.3.1-02.2016

Example 2

Find the area of the figure that consists of a rectangle with a semicircle on top. Use 3.14 for π.

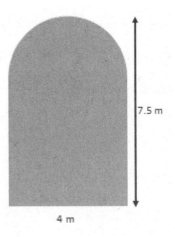

7.5 m

4 m

Exercise 2

Find the area of the shaded region. Use 3.14 for π.

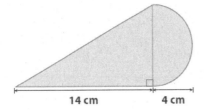

14 cm   4 cm

EUREKA
MATH™

© 2015 Great Minds. eureka-math.org
G7-M3M4-SE-B2-1.3.1-02.2016

Example 3

Find the area of the shaded region.

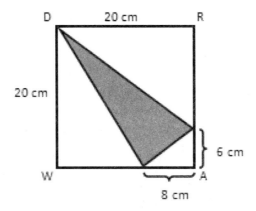

Redraw the figure separating the triangles; then, label the lengths discussing the calculations.

Exercise 3

Find the area of the shaded region. The figure is not drawn to scale.

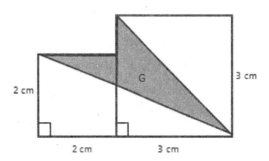

Problem Set

1. Find the area of the shaded region. Use 3.14 for π.

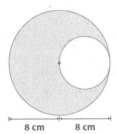

8 cm   8 cm

2. The figure shows two semicircles. Find the area of the shaded region. Use 3.14 for π.

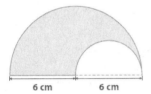

6 cm   6 cm

3. The figure shows a semicircle and a square. Find the area of the shaded region. Use 3.14 for π.

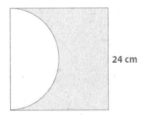

24 cm

4. The figure shows two semicircles and a quarter of a circle. Find the area of the shaded region. Use 3.14 for π.

10 cm   10 cm

EUREKA
MATH™

5. Jillian is making a paper flower motif for an art project. The flower she is making has four petals; each petal is formed by three semicircles as shown below. What is the area of the paper flower? Provide your answer in terms of π.

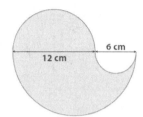

6. The figure is formed by five rectangles. Find the area of the unshaded rectangular region.

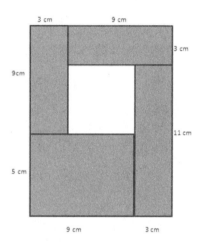

7. The smaller squares in the shaded region each have side lengths of 1.5 m. Find the area of the shaded region.

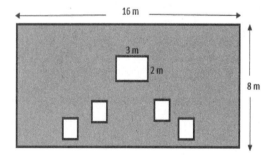

EUREKA
MATH™

Lesson 20:   Composite Area Problems

S.139

© 2015 Great Minds. eureka-math.org
G7-M3M4-SE-B2-1.3.1-02.2016

8. Find the area of the shaded region.

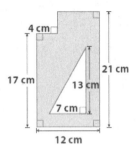

9.

a. Find the area of the shaded region.

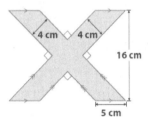

b. Draw two ways the figure above can be divided in four equal parts.

c. What is the area of one of the parts in (b)?

10. The figure is a rectangle made out of triangles. Find the area of the shaded region.

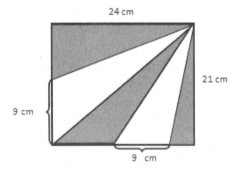

EUREKA
MATH™

11. The figure consists of a right triangle and an eighth of a circle. Find the area of the shaded region. Use $\frac{22}{7}$ for π.

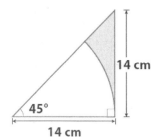

This page intentionally left blank

Lesson 21: Surface Area

Classwork

Opening Exercise: Surface Area of a Right Rectangular Prism

On the provided grid, draw a net representing the surfaces of the right rectangular prism (assume each grid line represents 1 inch). Then, find the surface area of the prism by finding the area of the net.

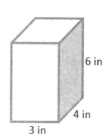

Exercise 1

Marcus thinks that the surface area of the right triangular prism will be half that of the right rectangular prism and wants to use the modified formula $SA = \frac{1}{2}(2lw + 2lh + 2wh)$. Do you agree or disagree with Marcus? Use nets of the prisms to support your argument.

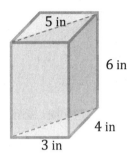

5 in
6 in
4 in
3 in

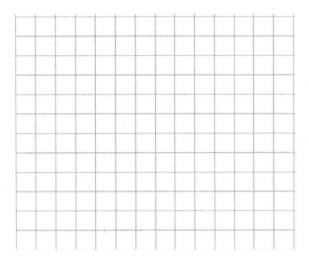

Example 1: Lateral Area of a Right Prism

A right triangular prism, a right rectangular prism, and a right pentagonal prism are pictured below, and all have equal heights of h.

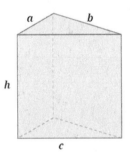
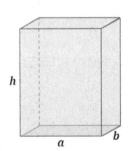
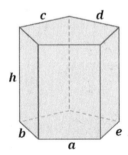

a.   Write an expression that represents the lateral area of the right triangular prism as the sum of the areas of its lateral faces.

EUREKA MATH™

b. Write an expression that represents the lateral area of the right rectangular prism as the sum of the areas of its lateral faces.

c. Write an expression that represents the lateral area of the right pentagonal prism as the sum of the areas of its lateral faces.

d. What value appears often in each expression and why?

e. Rewrite each expression in factored form using the distributive property and the height of each lateral face.

f. What do the parentheses in each case represent with respect to the right prisms?

g. How can we generalize the lateral area of a right prism into a formula that applies to all right prisms?

Relevant Vocabulary

RIGHT PRISM: Let E and E' be two parallel planes. Let B be a triangular or rectangular region or a region that is the union of such regions in the plane E. At each point P of B, consider the segment PP' perpendicular to E, joining P to a point P' of the plane E'. The union of all these segments is a solid called a *right prism*.

There is a region B' in E' that is an exact copy of the region B. The regions B and B' are called the *base faces* (or just *bases*) of the prism. The rectangular regions between two corresponding sides of the bases are called *lateral faces* of the prism. In all, the boundary of a right rectangular prism has 6 *faces*: 2 base faces and 4 lateral faces. All adjacent faces intersect along segments called *edges* (base edges and lateral edges).

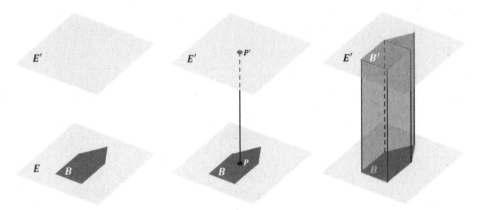

CUBE: A *cube* is a right rectangular prism all of whose edges are of equal length.

SURFACE: The *surface of a prism* is the union of all of its faces (the base faces and lateral faces).

NET: A *net* is a two-dimensional diagram of the surface of a prism.

1. Why are the lateral faces of right prisms always rectangular regions?

2. What is the name of the right prism whose bases are rectangles?

3. How does this definition of right prism include the interior of the prism?

Problem Set

1. For each of the following nets, highlight the perimeter of the lateral area, draw the solid represented by the net, indicate the type of solid, and then find the solid's surface area.

   a.

   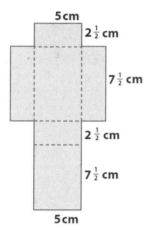

   b.

   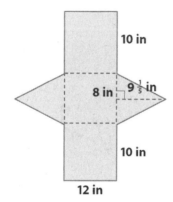

© 2015 Great Minds. eureka-math.org
G7-M3M4-SE-B2-1.3.1-02.2016

2. Given a cube with edges that are $\frac{3}{4}$ inch long:

   a. Find the surface area of the cube.

   b. Joshua makes a scale drawing of the cube using a scale factor of 4. Find the surface area of the cube that Joshua drew.

   c. What is the ratio of the surface area of the scale drawing to the surface area of the actual cube, and how does the value of the ratio compare to the scale factor?

3. Find the surface area of each of the following right prisms using the formula $SA = LA + 2B$.

   a.

   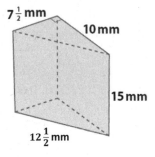

   b.

   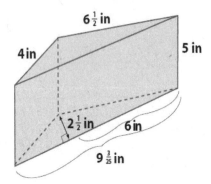

   c.

   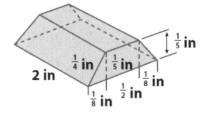

EUREKA
MATH

d.

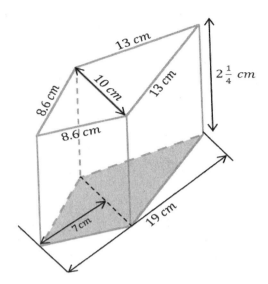

4. A cube has a volume of 64 m^3. What is the cube's surface area?

5. The height of a right rectangular prism is $4\frac{1}{2}$ ft. The length and width of the prism's base are 2 ft. and $1\frac{1}{2}$ ft. Use the formula $SA = LA + 2B$ to find the surface area of the right rectangular prism.

6. The surface area of a right rectangular prism is $68\frac{2}{3}$ in^2. The dimensions of its base are 3 in. and 7 in. Use the formula $SA = LA + 2B$ and $LA = Ph$ to find the unknown height h of the prism.

7. A given right triangular prism has an equilateral triangular base. The height of that equilateral triangle is approximately 7.1 cm. The distance between the bases is 9 cm. The surface area of the prism is $319\frac{1}{2}$ cm^2. Find the approximate lengths of the sides of the base.

This page intentionally left blank

Lesson 22: Surface Area

Opening Exercise

What is the area of the composite figure in the diagram? Is the diagram a net for a three-dimensional image? If so, sketch the image. If not, explain why.

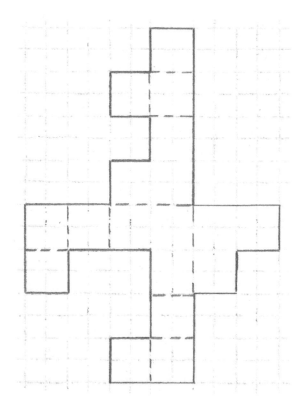

Example 1

The pyramid in the picture has a square base, and its lateral faces are triangles that are exact copies of one another. Find the surface area of the pyramid.

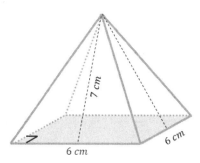

Example 2: Using Cubes

There are 13 cubes glued together forming the solid in the diagram. The edges of each cube are $\frac{1}{4}$ inch in length. Find the surface area of the solid.

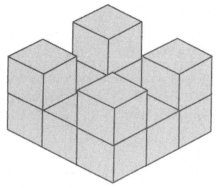

Example 3

Find the total surface area of the wooden jewelry box. The sides and bottom of the box are all $\frac{1}{4}$ inch thick.

What are the faces that make up this box?

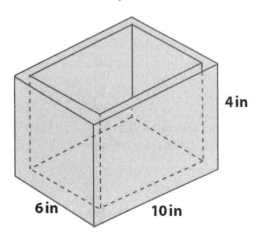

4 in

6 in   10 in

How does this box compare to other objects that you have found the surface area of?

EUREKA
MATH™

Large Prism

Small Prism

Surface Area of the Box

Problem Set

1. For each of the following nets, draw (or describe) the solid represented by the net and find its surface area.

   a. The equilateral triangles are exact copies.

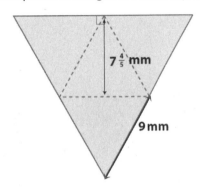

   b.

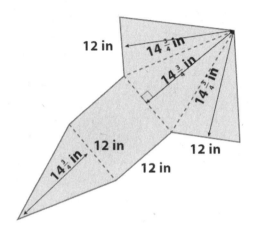

2. Find the surface area of the following prism.

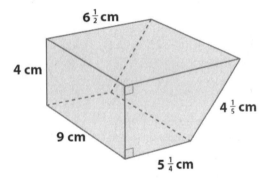

3. The net below is for a specific object. The measurements shown are in meters. Sketch (or describe) the object, and then find its surface area.

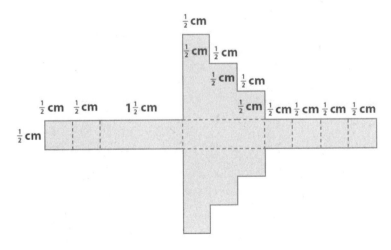

4. In the diagram, there are 14 cubes glued together to form a solid. Each cube has a volume of $\frac{1}{8}\text{in}^3$. Find the surface area of the solid.

5. The nets below represent three solids. Sketch (or describe) each solid, and find its surface area.

a.

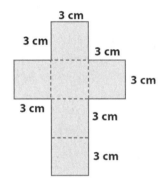

b.

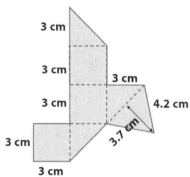

c.

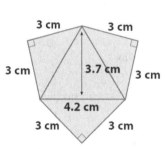

d. How are figures (b) and (c) related to figure (a)?

6. Find the surface area of the solid shown in the diagram. The solid is a right triangular prism (with right triangular bases) with a smaller right triangular prism removed from it.

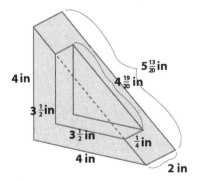

7.   The diagram shows a cubic meter that has had three square holes punched completely through the cube on three perpendicular axes. Find the surface area of the remaining solid.

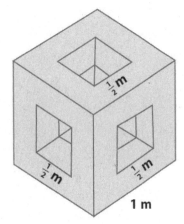

EUREKA
MATH™

Lesson 23: The Volume of a Right Prism

Classwork

Opening Exercise

The volume of a solid is a quantity given by the number of unit cubes needed to fill the solid. Most solids—rocks, baseballs, people—cannot be filled with unit cubes or assembled from cubes. Yet such solids still have volume. Fortunately, we do not need to assemble solids from unit cubes in order to calculate their volume. One of the first interesting examples of a solid that cannot be assembled from cubes, but whose volume can still be calculated from a formula, is a right triangular prism.

What is the area of the square pictured on the right? Explain.

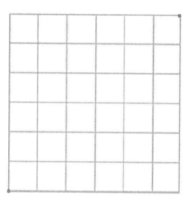

Draw the diagonal joining the two given points; then, darken the grid lines within the lower triangular region. What is the area of that triangular region? Explain.

Exploratory Challenge: The Volume of a Right Prism

What is the volume of the right prism pictured on the right? Explain.

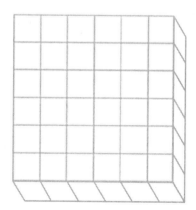

Draw the same diagonal on the square base as done above; then, darken the grid lines on the lower right triangular prism. What is the volume of that right triangular prism? Explain.

How could we create a right triangular prism with five times the volume of the right triangular prism pictured to the right, without changing the base? Draw your solution on the diagram, give the volume of the solid, and explain why your solution has five times the volume of the triangular prism.

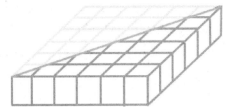

What could we do to cut the volume of the right triangular prism pictured on the right in half without changing the base? Draw your solution on the diagram, give the volume of the solid, and explain why your solution has half the volume of the given triangular prism.

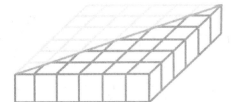

To find the volume (V) of any right prism …

EUREKA
MATH™

© 2015 Great Minds. eureka-math.org
G7-M3M4-SE-B2-1.3.1-02.2016

Example: The Volume of a Right Triangular Prism

Find the volume of the right triangular prism shown in the diagram using $V = Bh$.

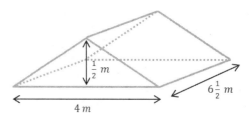

Exercise: Multiple Volume Representations

The right pentagonal prism is composed of a right rectangular prism joined with a right triangular prism. Find the volume of the right pentagonal prism shown in the diagram using two different strategies.

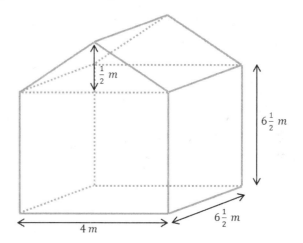

Problem Set

1. Calculate the volume of each solid using the formula $V = Bh$ (all angles are 90 degrees).

a.
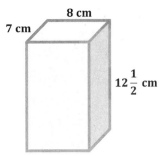

8 cm
7 cm
$12\frac{1}{2}$ cm

b.
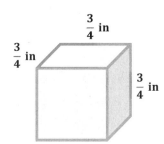

$\frac{3}{4}$ in
$\frac{3}{4}$ in
$\frac{3}{4}$ in

c.
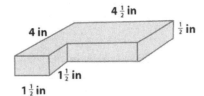

$4\frac{1}{2}$ in
4 in
$\frac{1}{2}$ in
$1\frac{1}{2}$ in
$1\frac{1}{2}$ in

d.
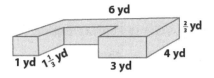

6 yd
$\frac{2}{3}$ yd
1 yd $1\frac{1}{3}$ yd
3 yd
4 yd

e.
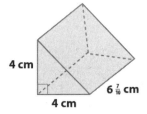

4 cm
4 cm
$6\frac{7}{10}$ cm

f.
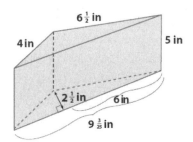

$6\frac{1}{2}$ in
4 in
5 in
$2\frac{1}{2}$ in
6 in
$9\frac{3}{25}$ in

g.
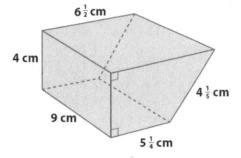

$6\frac{1}{2}$ cm
4 cm
$4\frac{1}{5}$ cm
9 cm
$5\frac{1}{4}$ cm

h.
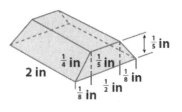

$\frac{1}{5}$ in
$\frac{1}{4}$ in $\frac{1}{5}$ in
2 in
$\frac{1}{8}$ in
$\frac{1}{8}$ in $\frac{1}{2}$ in

EUREKA
MATH™

2. Let l represent the length, w the width, and h the height of a right rectangular prism. Find the volume of the prism when

   a. $l = 3$ cm, $w = 2\frac{1}{2}$ cm, and $h = 7$ cm.

   b. $l = \frac{1}{4}$ cm, $w = 4$ cm, and $h = 1\frac{1}{2}$ cm.

3. Find the length of the edge indicated in each diagram.

   a.

   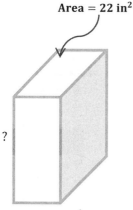

   Area = 22 in²

   Volume $= 93\frac{1}{2}$ **in³**

   What are possible dimensions of the base?

   b.

   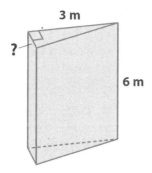

   3 m

   ?

   6 m

   Volume = 4½ m³

4. The volume of a cube is $3\frac{3}{8}$ in³. Find the length of each edge of the cube.

5. Given a right rectangular prism with a volume of $7\frac{1}{2}$ ft³, a length of 5 ft, and a width of 2 ft, find the height of the prism.

© 2015 Great Minds. eureka-math.org
G7-M3M4-SE-B2-1.3.1-02.2016

This page intentionally left blank

Lesson 24: The Volume of a Right Prism

Exploratory Challenge: Measuring a Container's Capacity

A box in the shape of a right rectangular prism has a length of 12 in, a width of 6 in, and a height of 8 in The base and the walls of the container are $\frac{1}{4}$ in. thick, and its top is open. What is the capacity of the right rectangular prism? (Hint: The capacity is equal to the volume of water needed to fill the prism to the top.)

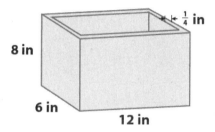

Example 1: Measuring Liquid in a Container in Three Dimensions

A glass container is in the form of a right rectangular prism. The container is 10 cm long, 8 cm wide, and 30 cm high. The top of the container is open, and the base and walls of the container are 3 mm (or 0.3 cm) thick. The water in the container is 6 cm from the top of the container. What is the volume of the water in the container?

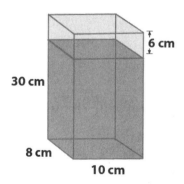

Example 2

7.2 L of water are poured into a container in the shape of a right rectangular prism. The inside of the container is 50 cm long, 20 cm wide, and 25 cm tall. How far from the top of the container is the surface of the water? (1 L = 1000 cm^3)

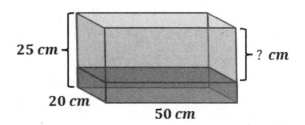

Example 3

A fuel tank is the shape of a right rectangular prism and has 27 L of fuel in it. It is determined that the tank is $\frac{3}{4}$ full. The inside dimensions of the base of the tank are 90 cm by 50 cm. What is the height of the fuel in the tank? How deep is the tank? (1 L = 1,000 cm^3)

© 2015 Great Minds. eureka-math.org
G7-M3M4-SE-B2-1.3.1-02.2016

Problem Set

1. Mark wants to put some fish and decorative rocks in his new glass fish tank. He measured the outside dimensions of the right rectangular prism and recorded a length of 55 cm, width of 42 cm, and height of 38 cm. He calculates that the tank will hold 87.78 L of water. Why is Mark's calculation of volume incorrect? What is the correct volume? Mark also failed to take into account the fish and decorative rocks he plans to add. How will this affect the volume of water in the tank? Explain.

2. Leondra bought an aquarium that is a right rectangular prism. The inside dimensions of the aquarium are 90 cm long, by 48 cm wide, by 60 cm deep. She plans to put water in the aquarium before purchasing any pet fish. How many liters of water does she need to put in the aquarium so that the water level is 5 cm below the top?

3. The inside space of two different water tanks are shown below. Which tank has a greater capacity? Justify your answer.

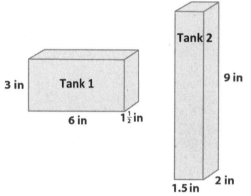

4. The inside of a tank is in the shape of a right rectangular prism. The base of that prism is 85 cm by 64 cm. What is the minimum height inside the tank If the volume of the liquid in the tank is 92 L ?

5. An oil tank is the shape of a right rectangular prism. The inside of the tank is 36.5 cm long, 52 cm wide, and 29 cm high. If 45 liters of oil have been removed from the tank since it was full, what is the current depth of oil left in the tank?

6. The inside of a right rectangular prism-shaped tank has a base that is 14 cm by 24 cm and a height of 60 cm. The tank is filled to its capacity with water, and then 10.92 L of water is removed. How far did the water level drop?

7. A right rectangular prism-shaped container has inside dimensions of $7\frac{1}{2}$ cm long and $4\frac{3}{5}$ cm wide. The tank is $\frac{3}{5}$ full of vegetable oil. It contains 0.414 L of oil. Find the height of the container.

8. A right rectangular prism with length of 10 in, width of 16 in, and height of 12 in is $\frac{2}{3}$ filled with water. If the water is emptied into another right rectangular prism with a length of 12 in., a width of 12 in., and height of 9 in., will the second container hold all of the water? Explain why or why not. Determine how far (above or below) the water level would be from the top of the container.

This page intentionally left blank

Lesson 25: Volume and Surface Area

Classwork

Opening Exercise

What is the surface area and volume of the right rectangular prism?

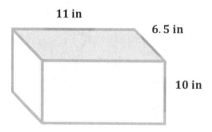

11 in

6.5 in

10 in

Example 1: Volume of a Fish Tank

Jay has a small fish tank. It is the same shape and size as the right rectangular prism shown in the Opening Exercise.

a. The box it came in says that it is a 3-gallon tank. Is this claim true? Explain your reasoning. Recall that $1 \text{ gal} = 231 \text{ in}^3$.

b. The pet store recommends filling the tank to within 1.5 in. of the top. How many gallons of water will the tank hold if it is filled to the recommended level?

c. Jay wants to cover the back, left, and right sides of the tank with a background picture. How many square inches will be covered by the picture?

d. Water in the tank evaporates each day, causing the water level to drop. How many gallons of water have evaporated by the time the water in the tank is four inches deep? Assume the tank was filled to within 1.5 in. of the top to start.

Exercise 1: Fish Tank Designs

Two fish tanks are shown below, one in the shape of a right rectangular prism (R) and one in the shape of a right trapezoidal prism (T).

Tank R

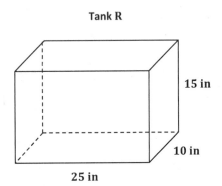

Tank T

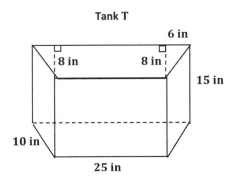

a. Which tank holds the most water? Let $Vol(R)$ represent the volume of the right rectangular prism and $Vol(T)$ represent the volume of the right trapezoidal prism. Use your answer to fill in the blanks with $Vol(R)$ and $Vol(T)$.

_____ < _____

b. Which tank has the most surface area? Let $SA(R)$ represent the surface area of the right rectangular prism and $SA(T)$ represent the surface area of the right trapezoidal prism. Use your answer to fill in the blanks with $SA(R)$ and $SA(T)$.

_____ < _____

c. Water evaporates from each aquarium. After the water level has dropped $\frac{1}{2}$ inch in each aquarium, how many cubic inches of water are required to fill up each aquarium? Show work to support your answers.

Exercise 2: Design Your Own Fish Tank

Design at least three fish tanks that will hold approximately 10 gallons of water. All of the tanks should be shaped like right prisms. Make at least one tank have a base that is not a rectangle. For each tank, make a sketch, and calculate the volume in gallons to the nearest hundredth.

Challenge: Each tank is to be constructed from glass that is $\frac{1}{4}$ in. thick. Select one tank that you designed, and determine the difference between the volume of the total tank (including the glass) and the volume inside the tank. Do not include a glass top on your tank.

EUREKA
MATH™

Problem Set

1. The dimensions of several right rectangular fish tanks are listed below. Find the volume in cubic centimeters, the capacity in liters (1 L = 1,000 cm³), and the surface area in square centimeters for each tank. What do you observe about the change in volume compared with the change in surface area between the small tank and the extra-large tank?

Tank Size	Length (cm)	Width (cm)	Height (cm)
Small	24	18	15
Medium	30	21	20
Large	36	24	25
Extra-Large	40	27	30

Tank Size	Volume (cm³)	Capacity (L)	Surface Area (cm²)
Small			
Medium			
Large			
Extra-Large			

2. A rectangular container 15 cm long by 25 cm wide contains 2.5 L of water.

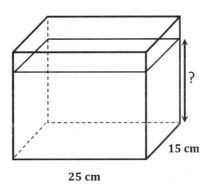

?

15 cm

25 cm

a. Find the height of the water level in the container. (1 L = 1,000 cm³)

b. If the height of the container is 18 cm, how many more liters of water would it take to completely fill the container?

c. What percentage of the tank is filled when it contains 2.5 L of water?

3. A rectangular container measuring 20 cm by 14.5 cm by 10.5 cm is filled with water to its brim. If 300 cm³ are drained out of the container, what will be the height of the water level? If necessary, round to the nearest tenth.

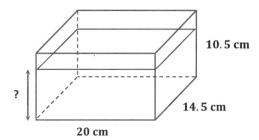

4. Two tanks are shown below. Both are filled to capacity, but the owner decides to drain them. Tank 1 is draining at a rate of 8 liters per minute. Tank 2 is draining at a rate of 10 liters per minute. Which tank empties first?

Tank 1   Tank 2

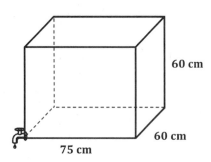   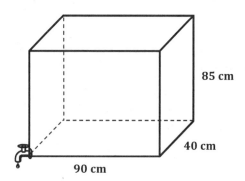

5. Two tanks are shown below. One tank is draining at a rate of 8 liters per minute into the other one, which is empty. After 10 minutes, what will be the height of the water level in the second tank? If necessary, round to the nearest minute.

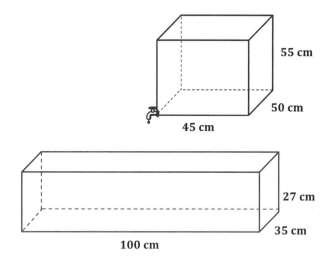

6. Two tanks with equal volumes are shown below. The tops are open. The owner wants to cover one tank with a glass top. The cost of glass is $0.05 per square inch. Which tank would be less expensive to cover? How much less?

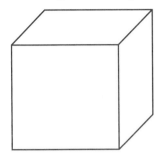   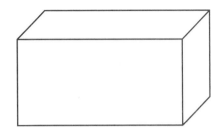

Dimensions: 12 in. long by 8 in. wide by 10 in. high   Dimensions: 15 in. long by 8 in. wide by 8 in. high

7. Each prism below is a gift box sold at the craft store.

(a)   (b)

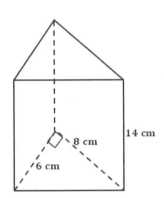   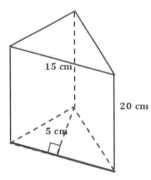

(c)   (d)

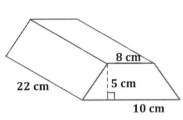   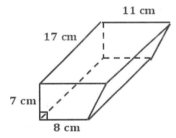

a. What is the volume of each prism?

b. Jenny wants to fill each box with jelly beans. If one ounce of jelly beans is approximately 30 cm^3, estimate how many ounces of jelly beans Jenny will need to fill all four boxes? Explain your estimates.

8. Two rectangular tanks are filled at a rate of 0.5 cubic inches per minute. How long will it take each tank to be half-full?

a. Tank 1 Dimensions: 15 in by 10 in by 12.5 in

b. Tank 2 Dimensions: $2\frac{1}{2}$ in by $3\frac{3}{4}$ in by $4\frac{3}{8}$ in

This page intentionally left blank

Lesson 26: Volume and Surface Area

Opening Exercise

Explain to your partner how you would calculate the area of the shaded region. Then, calculate the area.

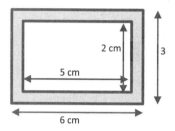

Example 1: Volume of a Shell

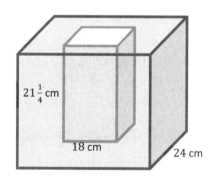

Top View

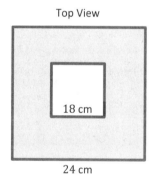

The insulated box shown is made from a large cube with a hollow inside that is a right rectangular prism with a square base. The figure on the right is what the box looks like from above.

a.   Calculate the volume of the outer box.

b.   Calculate the volume of the inner prism.

EUREKA
MATH™

Lesson 26:   Volume and Surface Area

S.175

© 2015 Great Minds. eureka-math.org
G7-M3M4-SE-B2-1.3.1-02.2016

c. Describe in words how you would find the volume of the insulation.

d. Calculate the volume of the insulation in cubic centimeters.

e. Calculate the amount of water the box can hold in liters.

Exercise 1: Brick Planter Design

You have been asked by your school to design a brick planter that will be used by classes to plant flowers. The planter will be built in the shape of a right rectangular prism with no bottom so water and roots can access the ground beneath. The exterior dimensions are to be 12 ft. × 9 ft. × $2\frac{1}{2}$ ft. The bricks used to construct the planter are 6 in. long, $3\frac{1}{2}$ in. wide, and 2 in. high.

a. What are the interior dimensions of the planter if the thickness of the planter's walls is equal to the length of the bricks?

b. What is the volume of the bricks that form the planter?

© 2015 Great Minds. eureka-math.org
G7-M3M4-SE-B2-1.3.1-02.2016

c. If you are going to fill the planter $\frac{3}{4}$ full of soil, how much soil will you need to purchase, and what will be the height of the soil?

d. How many bricks are needed to construct the planter?

e. Each brick used in this project costs $0.82 and weighs 4.5 lb. The supply company charges a delivery fee of $15 per whole ton (2,000 lb.) over 4,000 lb. How much will your school pay for the bricks (including delivery) to construct the planter?

© 2015 Great Minds. eureka-math.org
G7-M3M4-SE-B2-1.3.1-02.2016

f.   A cubic foot of topsoil weighs between 75 and 100 lb. How much will the soil in the planter weigh?

g.   If the topsoil costs $0.88 per each cubic foot, calculate the total cost of materials that will be used to construct the planter.

Exercise 2: Design a Feeder

You did such a good job designing the planter that a local farmer has asked you to design a feeder for the animals on his farm. Your feeder must be able to contain at least 100,000 cubic centimeters, but not more than 200,000 cubic centimeters of grain when it is full. The feeder is to be built of stainless steel and must be in the shape of a right prism but not a right rectangular prism. Sketch your design below including dimensions. Calculate the volume of grain that it can hold and the amount of metal needed to construct the feeder.

The farmer needs a cost estimate. Calculate the cost of constructing the feeder if $\frac{1}{2}$ cm thick stainless steel sells for $93.25 per square meter.

© 2015 Great Minds. eureka-math.org
G7-M3M4-SE-B2-1.3.1-02.2016

Problem Set

1. A child's toy is constructed by cutting a right triangular prism out of a right rectangular prism.

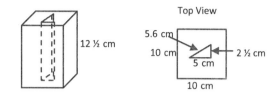

    a. Calculate the volume of the rectangular prism.

    b. Calculate the volume of the triangular prism.

    c. Calculate the volume of the material remaining in the rectangular prism.

    d. What is the largest number of triangular prisms that can be cut from the rectangular prism?

    e. What is the surface area of the triangular prism (assume there is no top or bottom)?

2. A landscape designer is constructing a flower bed in the shape of a right trapezoidal prism. He needs to run three identical square prisms through the bed for drainage.

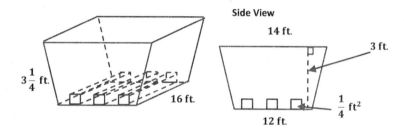

    a. What is the volume of the bed without the drainage pipes?

    b. What is the total volume of the three drainage pipes?

    c. What is the volume of soil if the planter is filled to $\frac{3}{4}$ of its total capacity with the pipes in place?

    d. What is the height of the soil? If necessary, round to the nearest tenth.

    e. If the bed is made of 8 ft. × 4 ft. pieces of plywood, how many pieces of plywood will the landscape designer need to construct the bed without the drainage pipes?

    f. If the plywood needed to construct the bed costs $35 per 8 ft. × 4 ft. piece, the drainage pipes cost $125 each, and the soil costs $1.25/cubic foot, how much does it cost to construct and fill the bed?

This page intentionally left blank

Eureka Math
Grade 7
Module 4

Special thanks go to the Gordon A. Cain Center and to the Department of Mathematics at Louisiana State University for their support in the development of *Eureka Math*.

For a free *Eureka Math* Teacher
Resource Pack, Parent Tip
Sheets, and more please
visit www.Eureka.tools

Lesson 1: Percent

Classwork

Opening Exercise 1: Matching

Match the percents with the correct sentence clues.

25%	I am half of a half. 5 cubic inches of water filled in a 20 cubic inch bottle.
50%	I am less than $\dfrac{1}{100}$. 25 out of 5,000 contestants won a prize.
30%	I am the chance of birthing a boy or a girl. Flip a coin, and it will land on heads or tails.
1%	I am less than a half but more than one-fourth. 15 out of 50 play drums in a band.
10%	I am equal to 1. 35 question out of 35 questions were answered correctly.
100%	I am more than 1. Instead of the \$1,200 expected to be raised, \$3,600 was collected for the school's fundraiser.
300%	I am a tenth of a tenth. One penny is this part of one dollar.
$\dfrac{1}{2}$%	I am less than a fourth but more than a hundredth. \$11 out of \$110 earned is saved in the bank.

Opening Exercise 2

Color in the grids to represent the following fractions:

a. $\dfrac{30}{100}$

b. $\dfrac{3}{100}$

c. $\dfrac{\frac{1}{3}}{100}$

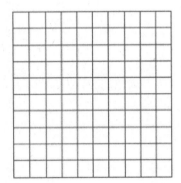   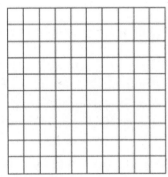   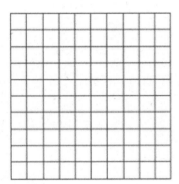

Example 1

Use the definition of the word *percent* to write each percent as a fraction and then as a decimal.

Percent	Fraction	Decimal
37.5%		
100%		
110%		
1%		
$\frac{1}{2}\%$		

EUREKA
MATH™

Example 2

Fill in the chart by converting between fractions, decimals, and percents. Show your work in the space below.

Fraction	Decimal	Percent
		350%
	0.025	
$\frac{1}{8}$		

© 2015 Great Minds. eureka-math.org
G7-M3M4-SE-B2-1.3.1-02.2016

Exercise: Class Card Activity

Read your card to yourself (each student has a different card), and work out the problem. When the exercise begins, listen carefully to the questions being read. When you have the card with the equivalent value, respond by reading your card aloud.

Examples:

0.22 should be read "twenty-two hundredths."

$\dfrac{\frac{1}{5}}{1000}$ should be read "one-fifth thousandths" or "one-fifth over one thousand."

$\dfrac{7}{300}$ should be read "seven three-hundredths" or "seven over three hundred."

$\dfrac{200}{100}$ should be read "two hundred hundredths" or "two hundred over one hundred."

EUREKA
MATH™

Lesson Summary

- One percent is the number $\frac{1}{100}$ and is written 1%. The number P% is the same as the number $\frac{P}{100}$.
- Usually, there are three ways to write a number: a percent, a fraction, and a decimal. The fraction and decimal forms of P% are equivalent to $\frac{P}{100}$.

Problem Set

1. Create a model to represent the following percents.

    a.   90%   b.   0.9%   c.   900%   d. $\frac{9}{10}$%

2. Benjamin believes that $\frac{1}{2}$% is equivalent to 50%. Is he correct? Why or why not?

3. Order the following from least to greatest:

    100%, $\frac{1}{100}$, 0.001%, $\frac{1}{10}$, 0.001, 1.1, 10, and $\frac{10,000}{100}$

4. Fill in the chart by converting between fractions, decimals, and percents. Show work in the space below.

Fraction	Decimal	Percent
		100%
	0.0825	
	6.25	
		$\frac{1}{8}$%
$\frac{2}{300}$		
		33.3%
$\frac{\frac{3}{4}}{100}$		
		250%
	0.005	
$\frac{150}{100}$		
	0.055	

This page intentionally left blank

Lesson 2: Part of a Whole as a Percent

Classwork

Opening Exercise

a. What is the whole unit in each scenario?

Scenario	Whole Unit
15 is what percent of 90?	
What number is 10% of 56?	
90% of a number is 180.	
A bag of candy contains 300 pieces and 25% of the pieces in the bag are red.	
Seventy percent (70%) of the students earned a B on the test.	
The 20 girls in the class represented 55% of the students in the class.	

b. Read each problem, and complete the table to record what you know.

Problem	Part	Percent	Whole
40% of the students on the field trip love the museum. If there are 20 students on the field trip, how many love the museum?			
40% of the students on the field trip love the museum. If 20 students love the museum, how many are on the field trip?			
20 students on the field trip love the museum. If there are 40 students on the field trip, what percent love the museum?			

© 2015 Great Minds. eureka-math.org
G7-M3M4-SE-B2-1.3.1-02.2016

Example 1: Visual Approaches to Finding a Part, Given a Percent of the Whole

In Ty's math class, 20% of students earned an A on a test. If there were 30 students in the class, how many got an A?

Exercise 1

In Ty's art class, 12% of the Flag Day art projects received a perfect score. There were 25 art projects turned in by Ty's class. How many of the art projects earned a perfect score? (Identify the whole.)

© 2015 Great Minds. eureka-math.org
G7-M3M4-SE-B2-1.3.1-02.2016

Example 2: A Numeric Approach to Finding a Part, Given a Percent of the Whole

In Ty's English class, 70% of the students completed an essay by the due date. There are 30 students in Ty's English class. How many completed the essay by the due date?

Example 3: An Algebraic Approach to Finding a Part, Given a Percent of the Whole

A bag of candy contains 300 pieces of which 28% are red. How many pieces are red?

Which quantity represents the whole?

Which of the terms in the percent equation is unknown? Define a letter (variable) to represent the unknown quantity.

Write an expression using the percent and the whole to represent the number of pieces of red candy.

Write and solve an equation to find the unknown quantity.

Lesson 2:   Part of a Whole as a Percent   S.9

Exercise 2

A bag of candy contains 300 pieces of which 28% are red. How many pieces are not red?

    a.   Write an equation to represent the number of pieces that are not red, n.

    b.   Use your equation to find the number of pieces of candy that are not red.

    c.   Jah-Lil told his math teacher that he could use the answer from Example 3 and mental math to find the
         number of pieces of candy that are not red. Explain what Jah-Lil meant by that.

Example 4: Comparing Part of a Whole to the Whole with the Percent Formula

Zoey inflated 24 balloons for decorations at the middle school dance. If Zoey inflated 15% of the total number of
balloons inflated for the dance, how many balloons are there total? Solve the problem using the percent formula, and
verify your answer using a visual model.

Example 5: Finding the Percent Given a Part of the Whole and the Whole

Haley is making admission tickets to the middle school dance. So far she has made 112 tickets, and her plan is to make 320 tickets. What percent of the admission tickets has Haley produced so far? Solve the problem using the percent formula, and verify your answer using a visual model.

Lesson Summary

- Visual models or numeric methods can be used to solve percent problems.
- An equation can be used to solve percent problems:

$$\text{Part} = \text{Percent} \times \text{Whole}.$$

Problem Set

1. Represent each situation using an equation. Check your answer with a visual model or numeric method.
   a. What number is 40% of 90?
   b. What number is 45% of 90?
   c. 27 is 30% of what number?
   d. 18 is 30% of what number?
   e. 25.5 is what percent of 85?
   f. 21 is what percent of 60?

2. 40% of the students on a field trip love the museum. If there are 20 students on the field trip, how many love the museum?

3. Maya spent 40% of her savings to pay for a bicycle that cost her $85.
   a. How much money was in her savings to begin with?
   b. How much money does she have left in her savings after buying the bicycle?

4. Curtis threw 15 darts at a dartboard. 40% of his darts hit the bull's-eye. How many darts did not hit the bull's-eye?

5. A tool set is on sale for $424.15. The original price of the tool set was $499.00. What percent of the original price is the sale price?

6. Matthew scored a total of 168 points in basketball this season. He scored 147 of those points in the regular season, and the rest were scored in his only playoff game. What percent of his total points did he score in the playoff game?

7. Brad put 10 crickets in his pet lizard's cage. After one day, Brad's lizard had eaten 20% of the crickets he had put in the cage. By the end of the next day, the lizard had eaten 25% of the remaining crickets. How many crickets were left in the cage at the end of the second day?

8. A furnace used 40% of the fuel in its tank in the month of March and then used 25% of the remaining fuel in the month of April. At the beginning of March, there were 240 gallons of fuel in the tank. How much fuel (in gallons) was left at the end of April?

9. In Lewis County, there were 2,277 student athletes competing in spring sports in 2014. That was 110% of the number from 2013, which was 90% of the number from the year before. How many student athletes signed up for a spring sport in 2012?

10. Write a real-world word problem that could be modeled by the equation below. Identify the elements of the percent equation and where they appear in your word problem, and then solve the problem.

$$57.5 = p(250)$$

This page intentionally left blank

Lesson 3: Comparing Quantities with Percent

Opening Exercise

If each 10 × 10 unit square represents one whole, then what percent is represented by the shaded region?

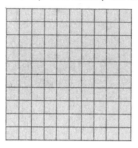 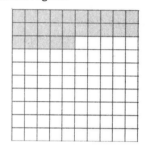

In the model above, 25% represents a quantity of 10 students. How many students does the shaded region represent?

Example

a. The members of a club are making friendship bracelets to sell to raise money. Anna and Emily made 54 bracelets over the weekend. They need to produce 300 bracelets by the end of the week. What percent of the bracelets were they able to produce over the weekend?

© 2015 Great Minds. eureka-math.org
G7-M3M4-SE-B2-1.3.1-02.2016

b. Anna produced 32 bracelets of the 54 bracelets produced by Emily and Anna over the weekend. Write the number of bracelets that Emily produced as a percent of those that Anna produced.

c. Write the number of bracelets that Anna produced as a percent of those that Emily produced.

Exercises

1. There are 750 students in the seventh-grade class and 625 students in the eighth-grade class at Kent Middle School.
    a. What percent is the seventh-grade class of the eighth-grade class at Kent Middle School?

    b. The principal will have to increase the number of eighth-grade teachers next year if the seventh-grade enrollment exceeds 110% of the current eighth-grade enrollment. Will she need to increase the number of teachers? Explain your reasoning.

2.   At Kent Middle School, there are 104 students in the band and 80 students in the choir. What percent of the number of students in the choir is the number of students in the band?

3.   At Kent Middle School, breakfast costs $1.25 and lunch costs $3.75. What percent of the cost of lunch is the cost of breakfast?

4.   Describe a real-world situation that could be modeled using the equation $398.4 = 0.83(x)$. Describe how the elements of the equation correspond with the real-world quantities in your problem. Then, solve your problem.

Lesson Summary

- Visual models or arithmetic methods can be used to solve problems that compare quantities with percents.
- Equations can be used to solve percent problems using the basic equation

$$\text{Quantity} = \text{Percent} \times \text{Whole}.$$

- *Quantity* in the new percent formula is the equivalent of *part* in the original percent formula.

Problem Set

1. Solve each problem using an equation.

   a. 49.5 is what percent of 33?

   b. 72 is what percent of 180?

   c. What percent of 80 is 90?

2. This year, Benny is 12 years old, and his mom is 48 years old.

   a. What percent of his mom's age is Benny's age?

   b. What percent of Benny's age is his mom's age?

   c. In two years, what percent of his age will Benny's mom's age be at that time?

   d. In 10 years, what percent will Benny's mom's age be of his age?

   e. In how many years will Benny be 50% of his mom's age?

   f. As Benny and his mom get older, Benny thinks that the percent of difference between their ages will decrease as well. Do you agree or disagree? Explain your reasoning.

3. This year, Benny is 12 years old. His brother Lenny's age is 175% of Benny's age. How old is Lenny?

4. When Benny's sister Penny is 24, Benny's age will be 125% of her age.

   a. How old will Benny be then?

   b. If Benny is 12 years old now, how old is Penny now? Explain your reasoning.

5. Benny's age is currently 200% of his sister Jenny's age. What percent of Benny's age will Jenny's age be in 4 years?

© 2015 Great Minds. eureka-math.org
G7-M3M4-SE-B2-1.3.1-02.2016

6. At an animal shelter, there are 15 dogs, 12 cats, 3 snakes, and 5 parakeets.

    a. What percent of the number of cats is the number of dogs?

    b. What percent of the number of cats is the number of snakes?

    c. What percent less parakeets are there than dogs?

    d. Which animal has 80% of the number of another animal?

    e. Which animal makes up approximately 14% of the animals in the shelter?

7. Is 2 hours and 30 minutes more or less than 10% of a day? Explain your answer.

8. A club's membership increased from 25 to 30 members.

    a. Express the new membership as a percent of the old membership.

    b. Express the old membership as a percent of the new membership.

9. The number of boys in a school is 120% the number of girls at the school.

    a. Find the number of boys if there are 320 girls.

    b. Find the number of girls if there are 360 boys.

10. The price of a bicycle was increased from $300 to $450.

    a. What percent of the original price is the increased price?

    b. What percent of the increased price is the original price?

11. The population of Appleton is 175% of the population of Cherryton.

    a. Find the population in Appleton if the population in Cherryton is 4,000 people.

    b. Find the population in Cherryton if the population in Appleton is 10,500 people.

12. A statistics class collected data regarding the number of boys and the number of girls in each classroom at their school during homeroom. Some of their results are shown in the table below.

   a. Complete the blank cells of the table using your knowledge about percent.

Number of Boys (x)	Number of Girls (y)	Number of Girls as a Percent of the Number of Boys
10	5	
	1	25%
18	12	
5	10	
4		50%
20		90%
	10	250%
	6	60%
11		200%
	5	$33\frac{1}{3}\%$
15		20%
	15	75%
6	18	
25	10	
10		110%
	2	10%
16		75%
	7	50%
3		200%
12	10	

   b. Using a coordinate plane and grid paper, locate and label the points representing the ordered pairs (x, y).

   c. Locate all points on the graph that would represent classrooms in which the number of girls y is 100% of the number of boys x. Describe the pattern that these points make.

d. Which points represent the classrooms in which the number of girls as a percent of the number of boys is greater than 100%? Which points represent the classrooms in which the number of girls as a percent of the number of boys is less than 100%? Describe the locations of the points in relation to the points in part (c).

e. Find three ordered pairs from your table representing classrooms where the number of girls is the same percent of the number of boys. Do these points represent a proportional relationship? Explain your reasoning.

f. Show the relationship(s) from part (e) on the graph, and label them with the corresponding equation(s).

g. What is the constant of proportionality in your equation(s), and what does it tell us about the number of girls and the number of boys at each point on the graph that represents it? What does the constant of proportionality represent in the table in part (a)?

This page intentionally left blank

Lesson 4: Percent Increase and Decrease

Opening Exercise

Cassandra likes jewelry. She has five rings in her jewelry box.

a. In the box below, sketch Cassandra's five rings.

b. Draw a double number line diagram relating the number of rings as a percent of the whole set of rings.

c. What percent is represented by the whole collection of rings? What percent of the collection does each ring represent?

Cassandra's aunt said she will buy Cassandra another ring for her birthday. If Cassandra gets the ring for her birthday, what will be the percent increase in her ring collection?

Exercise 1

a. Jon increased his trading card collection by 5 cards. He originally had 15 cards. What is the percent increase? Use the equation Quantity = Percent × Whole to arrive at your answer, and then justify your answer using a numeric or visual model.

b. Suppose instead of increasing the collection by 5 cards, Jon increased his 15-card collection by just 1 card. Will the percent increase be the same as when Cassandra's ring collection increased by 1 ring (in Example 1)? Why or why not? Explain.

c. Based on your answer to part (b), how is displaying change as a percent useful?

Discussion

A sales representative is taking 10% off of your bill as an apology for any inconveniences.

EUREKA
MATH™

© 2015 Great Minds. eureka-math.org
G7-M3M4-SE-B2-1.3.1-02.2016

Ken said that he is going to reduce the number of calories that he eats during the day. Ken's trainer asked him to start off small and reduce the number of calories by no more than 7%. Ken estimated and consumed 2,200 calories per day instead of his normal 2,500 calories per day until his next visit with the trainer. Did Ken reduce his calorie intake by no more than 7%? Justify your answer.

Exercise 2

Skylar is answering the following math problem:

The value of an investment decreased by 10%. *The original amount of the investment was* $75.00. *What is the current value of the investment?*

a. Skylar said 10% of $75.00 is $7.50, and since the investment decreased by that amount, you have to subtract $7.50 from $75.00 to arrive at the final answer of $67.50. Create one algebraic equation that can be used to arrive at the final answer of $67.50. Solve the equation to prove it results in an answer of $67.50. Be prepared to explain your thought process to the class.

b.   Skylar wanted to show the proportional relationship between the dollar value of the original investment, x, and its value after a 10% decrease, y. He creates the table of values shown. Does it model the relationship? Explain. Then, provide a correct equation for the relationship Skylar wants to model.

x	y
75	7.5
100	10
200	20
300	30
400	40

Example 3: Finding a Percent Increase or Decrease

Justin earned 8 badges in Scouts as of the Scout Master's last report. Justin wants to complete 2 more badges so that he will have a total of 10 badges earned before the Scout Master's next report.

a.   If Justin completes the additional 2 badges, what will be the percent increase in badges?

b.   Express the 10 badges as a percent of the 8 badges.

c.   Does 100% plus your answer in part (a) equal your answer in part (b)? Why or why not?

The population of cats in a rural neighborhood has declined in the past year by roughly 30%. Residents hypothesize that this is due to wild coyotes preying on the cats. The current cat population in the neighborhood is estimated to be 12. Approximately how many cats were there originally?

© 2015 Great Minds. eureka-math.org
G7-M3M4-SE-B2-1.3.1-02.2016

Example 5: Finding the Original Amount Given a Percent Increase or Decrease

Lu's math score on her achievement test in seventh grade was a 650. Her math teacher told her that her test level went up by 25% from her sixth grade test score level. What was Lu's test score level in sixth grade?

Closing

Phrase	Whole Unit (100%)
"Mary has 20% more money than John."	
"Anne has 15% less money than John."	
"What percent more (money) does Anne have than Bill?"	
"What percent less (money) does Bill have than Anne?"	

EUREKA
MATH™

© 2015 Great Minds. eureka-math.org
G7-M3M4-SE-B2-1.3.1-02.2016

Lesson Summary

- Within each problem, there are keywords that determine if the problem represents a percent increase or a percent decrease.
- Equations can be used to solve percent problems using the basic equation

$$\text{Quantity} = \text{Percent} \times \text{Whole.}$$

- *Quantity* in the percent formula is the amount of change (increase or decrease) or the amount after the change.
- *Whole* in the percent formula represents the original amount.

Problem Set

1. A store advertises 15% off an item that regularly sells for $300.

    a. What is the sale price of the item?
    b. How is a 15% discount similar to a 15% decrease? Explain.
    c. If 8% sales tax is charged on the sale price, what is the total with tax?
    d. How is 8% sales tax like an 8% increase? Explain.

2. An item that was selling for $72.00 is reduced to $60.00. Find the percent decrease in price. Round your answer to the nearest tenth.

3. A baseball team had 80 players show up for tryouts last year and this year had 96 players show up for tryouts. Find the percent increase in players from last year to this year.

4. At a student council meeting, there was a total of 60 students present. Of those students, 35 were female.

    a. By what percent is the number of females greater than the number of males?
    b. By what percent is the number of males less than the number of females?
    c. Why is the percent increase and percent decrease in parts (a) and (b) different?

5. Once each day, Darlene writes in her personal diary and records whether the sun is shining or not. When she looked back though her diary, she found that over a period of 600 days, the sun was shining 60% of the time. She kept recording for another 200 days and then found that the total number of sunny days dropped to 50%. How many of the final 200 days were sunny days?

6. Henry is considering purchasing a mountain bike. He likes two bikes: One costs $500, and the other costs $600. He tells his dad that the bike that is more expensive is 20% more than the cost of the other bike. Is he correct? Justify your answer.

7. State two numbers such that the lesser number is 25% less than the greater number.

8. State two numbers such that the greater number is 75% more than the lesser number.

9. Explain the difference in your thought process for Problems 7 and 8. Can you use the same numbers for each problem? Why or why not?

10. In each of the following expressions, c represents the original cost of an item.

    i. $0.90c$

    ii. $0.10c$

    iii. $c - 0.10c$

    a. Circle the expression(s) that represents 10% of the original cost. If more than one answer is correct, explain why the expressions you chose are equivalent.

    b. Put a box around the expression(s) that represents the final cost of the item after a 10% decrease. If more than one is correct, explain why the expressions you chose are equivalent.

    c. Create a word problem involving a percent decrease so that the answer can be represented by expression (ii).

    d. Create a word problem involving a percent decrease so that the answer can be represented by expression (i).

    e. Tyler wants to know if it matters if he represents a situation involving a 25% decrease as $0.25x$ or $(1 - 0.25)x$. In the space below, write an explanation that would help Tyler understand how the context of a word problem often determines how to represent the situation.

© 2015 Great Minds. eureka-math.org
G7-M3M4-SE-B2-1.3.1-02.2016

Lesson 5: Finding One Hundred Percent Given Another Percent

Classwork

Opening Exercise

What are the whole number factors of 100? What are the multiples of those factors? How many multiples are there of each factor (up to 100)?

Factors of 100	Multiples of the Factors of 100	Number of Multiples
100	100	1
50	50, 100	2
1	1, 2, 3, 4, 5, 6, … , 98, 99, 100	100

Example 1: Using a Modified Double Number Line with Percents

The 42 students who play wind instruments represent 75% of the students who are in band. How many students are in band?

Exercises 1–3

1. Bob's Tire Outlet sold a record number of tires last month. One salesman sold 165 tires, which was 60% of the tires sold in the month. What was the record number of tires sold?

2. Nick currently has 7,200 points in his fantasy baseball league, which is 20% more points than Adam. How many points does Adam have?

3. Kurt has driven 276 miles of his road trip but has 70% of the trip left to go. How many more miles does Kurt have to drive to get to his destination?

Example 2: Mental Math Using Factors of 100

Answer each part below using only mental math, and describe your method.

   a.   If 39 is 1% of a number, what is that number? How did you find your answer?

   b.   If 39 is 10% of a number, what is that number? How did you find your answer?

   c.   If 39 is 5% of a number, what is that number? How did you find your answer?

   d.   If 39 is 15% of a number, what is that number? How did you find your answer?

   e.   If 39 is 25% of a number, what is that number? How did you find your answer?

Exercises 4–5

4. Derrick had a 0.250 batting average at the end of his last baseball season, which means that he got a hit 25% of the times he was up to bat. If Derrick had 47 hits last season, how many times did he bat?

5. Nelson used 35% of his savings account for his class trip in May. If he used $140 from his savings account while on his class trip, how much money was in his savings account before the trip?

EUREKA
MATH

Lesson Summary

To find 100% of the whole, you can use a variety of methods, including factors of 100 (1, 2, 4, 5, 10, 20, 25, 50, and 100) and double number lines. Both methods will require breaking 100% into equal-sized intervals. Use the greatest common factor of 100 and the percent corresponding to the part.

Problem Set

Use a double number line to answer Problems 1–5.

1. Tanner collected 360 cans and bottles while fundraising for his baseball team. This was 40% of what Reggie collected. How many cans and bottles did Reggie collect?

2. Emilio paid $287.50 in taxes to the school district that he lives in this year. This year's taxes were a 15% increase from last year. What did Emilio pay in school taxes last year?

3. A snowmobile manufacturer claims that its newest model is 15% lighter than last year's model. If this year's model weighs 799 lb., how much did last year's model weigh?

4. Student enrollment at a local school is concerning the community because the number of students has dropped to 504, which is a 20% decrease from the previous year. What was the student enrollment the previous year?

5. The color of paint used to paint a race car includes a mixture of yellow and green paint. Scotty wants to lighten the color by increasing the amount of yellow paint 30%. If a new mixture contains 3.9 liters of yellow paint, how many liters of yellow paint did he use in the previous mixture?

Use factors of 100 and mental math to answer Problems 6–10. Describe the method you used.

6. Alexis and Tasha challenged each other to a typing test. Alexis typed 54 words in one minute, which was 120% of what Tasha typed. How many words did Tasha type in one minute?

7. Yoshi is 5% taller today than she was one year ago. Her current height is 168 cm. How tall was she one year ago?

8. Toya can run one lap of the track in 1 min. 3 sec., which is 90% of her younger sister Niki's time. What is Niki's time for one lap of the track?

9. An animal shelter houses only cats and dogs, and there are 25% more cats than dogs. If there are 40 cats, how many dogs are there, and how many animals are there total?

---

10. Angie scored 91 points on a test but only received a 65% grade on the test. How many points were possible on the test?

For Problems 11–17, find the answer using any appropriate method.

11. Robbie owns 15% more movies than Rebecca, and Rebecca owns 10% more movies than Joshua. If Rebecca owns 220 movies, how many movies do Robbie and Joshua each have?

12. 20% of the seventh-grade students have math class in the morning. $16\frac{2}{3}$% of those students also have science class in the morning. If 30 seventh-grade students have math class in the morning but not science class, find how many seventh-grade students there are.

13. The school bookstore ordered three-ring notebooks. They put 75% of the order in the warehouse and sold 80% of the rest in the first week of school. There are 25 notebooks left in the store to sell. How many three-ring notebooks did they originally order?

14. In the first game of the year, the modified basketball team made 62.5% of their foul shot free throws. Matthew made all 6 of his free throws, which made up 25% of the team's free throws. How many free throws did the team miss altogether?

15. Aiden's mom calculated that in the previous month, their family had used 40% of their monthly income for gasoline, and 63% of that gasoline was consumed by the family's SUV. If the family's SUV used $261.45 worth of gasoline last month, how much money was left after gasoline expenses?

16. Rectangle A is a scale drawing of Rectangle B and has 25% of its area. If Rectangle A has side lengths of 4 cm and 5 cm, what are the side lengths of Rectangle B?

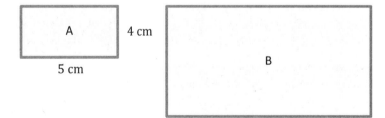

17. Ted is a supervisor and spends 20% of his typical work day in meetings and 20% of that meeting time in his daily team meeting. If he starts each day at 7:30 a.m., and his daily team meeting is from 8:00 a.m. to 8:20 a.m., when does Ted's typical work day end?

Lesson 6: Fluency with Percents

Opening Exercise

Solve the following problem using mental math only. Be prepared to discuss your method with your classmates.

Cory and Everett have collected model cars since the third grade. Cory has 80 model cars in his collection, which is 25% more than Everett has. How many model cars does Everett have?

Example 1: Mental Math and Percents

a.   75% of the students in Jesse's class are 60 inches or taller. If there are 20 students in her class, how many students are 60 inches or taller?

b.   Bobbie wants to leave a tip for her waitress equal to 15% of her bill. Bobbie's bill for her lunch is $18. How much money represents 15% of the bill?

© 2015 Great Minds. eureka-math.org
G7-M3M4-SE-B2-1.3.1-02.2016

Exercises

1. Express 9 hours as a percentage of 3 days.

2. Richard works from 11:00 a.m. to 3:00 a.m. His dinner break is 75% of the way through his work shift. What time is Richard's dinner break?

3. At a playoff basketball game, there were 370 fans cheering for school A and 555 fans cheering for school B.
    a.   Express the number of fans cheering for school A as a percent of the number of fans cheering for school B.

EUREKA
MATH

b.   Express the number of fans cheering for school B as a percent of the number of fans cheering for school A.

c.   What percent more fans were there for school B than for school A?

4.   Rectangle A has a width of 8 cm and a length of 16 cm. Rectangle B has the same area as the first, but its width is 62.5% of the width of the first rectangle. Express the length of Rectangle B as a percent of the length of Rectangle A. What percent more or less is the length of Rectangle B than the length of Rectangle A?

5. A plant in Mikayla's garden was 40 inches tall one day and was 4 feet tall one week later. By what percent did the plant's height increase over one week?

6. Loren must obtain a minimum number of signatures on a petition before it can be submitted. She was able to obtain 672 signatures, which is 40% more than she needs. How many signatures does she need?

© 2015 Great Minds. eureka-math.org
G7-M3M4-SE-B2-1.3.1-02.2016

Lesson Summary

- Identify the type of percent problem that is being asked as a comparison of quantities or a part of a whole.

- Identify what numbers represent the part, the whole, and the percent, and use the representation

  Quantity = Percent × Whole.

- A strategy to solving percents using mental math is to rewrite a percent using 1%, 5%, or 10%. These percents can be solved mentally. For example: $13\% = 10\% + 3(1\%)$. To find 13% of 70, find 10% of 70 as 7, 1% of 70 as 0.7, so 13% of 70 is $7 + 3(0.7) = 7 + 2.10 = 9.10$.

Problem Set

1. Micah has 294 songs stored in his phone, which is 70% of the songs that Jorge has stored in his phone. How many songs are stored on Jorge's phone?

2. Lisa sold 81 magazine subscriptions, which is 27% of her class's fundraising goal. How many magazine subscriptions does her class hope to sell?

3. Theresa and Isaiah are comparing the number of pages that they read for pleasure over the summer. Theresa read 2,210 pages, which was 85% of the number of pages that Isaiah read. How many pages did Isaiah read?

4. In a parking garage, the number of SUVs is 40% greater than the number of non-SUVs. Gina counted 98 SUVs in the parking garage. How many vehicles were parked in the garage?

5. The price of a tent was decreased by 15% and sold for $76.49. What was the original price of the tent in dollars?

6. 40% of the students at Rockledge Middle School are musicians. 75% of those musicians have to read sheet music when they play their instruments. If 38 of the students can play their instruments without reading sheet music, how many students are there at Rockledge Middle School?

7. At Longbridge Middle School, 240 students said that they are an only child, which is 48% of the school's student enrollment. How many students attend Longbridge Middle School?

8. Grace and her father spent $4\frac{1}{2}$ hours over the weekend restoring their fishing boat. This time makes up 6% of the time needed to fully restore the boat. How much total time is needed to fully restore the boat?

9. Bethany's mother was upset with her because Bethany's text messages from the previous month were 218% of the amount allowed at no extra cost under her phone plan. Her mother had to pay for each text message over the allowance. Bethany had 5,450 text messages last month. How many text messages is she allowed under her phone plan at no extra cost?

10. Harry used 84% of the money in his savings account to buy a used dirt bike that cost him $1,050. How much money is left in Harry's savings account?

11. 15% of the students in Mr. Riley's social studies classes watch the local news every night. Mr. Riley found that 136 of his students do not watch the local news. How many students are in Mr. Riley's social studies classes?

12. Grandma Bailey and her children represent about 9.1% of the Bailey family. If Grandma Bailey has 12 children, how many members are there in the Bailey family?

13. Shelley earned 20% more money in tips waitressing this week than last week. This week she earned $72.00 in tips waitressing. How much money did Shelley earn last week in tips?

14. Lucy's savings account has 35% more money than her sister Edy's. Together, the girls have saved a total of $206.80. How much money has each girl saved?

15. Bella spent 15% of her paycheck at the mall, and 40% of that was spent at the movie theater. Bella spent a total of $13.74 at the movie theater for her movie ticket, popcorn, and a soft drink. How much money was in Bella's paycheck?

16. On a road trip, Sara's brother drove 47.5% of the trip, and Sara drove 80% of the remainder. If Sara drove for 4 hours and 12 minutes, how long was the road trip?

Lesson 7: Markup and Markdown Problems

Classwork

Example 1: A Video Game Markup

Games Galore Super Store buys the latest video game at a wholesale price of $30.00. The markup rate at Game's Galore Super Store is 40%. You use your allowance to purchase the game at the store. How much will you pay, not including tax?

    a.   Write an equation to find the price of the game at Games Galore Super Store. Explain your equation.

    b.   Solve the equation from part (a).

    c.   What was the total markup of the video game? Explain.

    d.   You and a friend are discussing markup rate. He says that an easier way to find the total markup is by multiplying the wholesale price of $30.00 by 40%. Do you agree with him? Why or why not?

© 2015 Great Minds. eureka-math.org
G7-M3M4-SE-B2-1.3.1-02.2016

Example 2: Black Friday

A $300 mountain bike is discounted by 30% and then discounted an additional 10% for shoppers who arrive before 5:00 a.m.

   a.   Find the sales price of the bicycle.

   b.   In all, by how much has the bicycle been discounted in dollars? Explain.

   c.   After both discounts were taken, what was the total percent discount?

   d.   Instead of purchasing the bike for $300, how much would you save if you bought it before 5:00 a.m.?

EUREKA MATH

Exercises 1–3

1. Sasha went shopping and decided to purchase a set of bracelets for 25% off the regular price. If Sasha buys the bracelets today, she will save an additional 5%. Find the sales price of the set of bracelets with both discounts. How much money will Sasha save if she buys the bracelets today?

$44.00

2. A golf store purchases a set of clubs at a wholesale price of $250. Mr. Edmond learned that the clubs were marked up 200%. Is it possible to have a percent increase greater than 100%? What is the retail price of the clubs?

3. Is a percent increase of a set of golf clubs from $250 to $750 the same as a markup rate of 200%? Explain.

Example 3: Working Backward

A car that normally sells for $20,000 is on sale for $16,000. The sales tax is 7.5%.

    a.   What percent of the original price of the car is the final price?

    b.   Find the discount rate.

    c.   By law, sales tax has to be applied to the discount price. However, would it be better for the consumer if the 7.5% sales tax was calculated before the 20% discount was applied? Why or why not?

    d.   Write an equation applying the commutative property to support your answer to part (c).

© 2015 Great Minds. eureka-math.org
G7-M3M4-SE-B2-1.3.1-02.2016

Exercise 4

    a.   Write an equation to determine the selling price in dollars, p, on an item that is originally priced s dollars after a markup of 25%.

    b.   Create and label a table showing five possible pairs of solutions to the equation.

    c.   Create and label a graph of the equation.

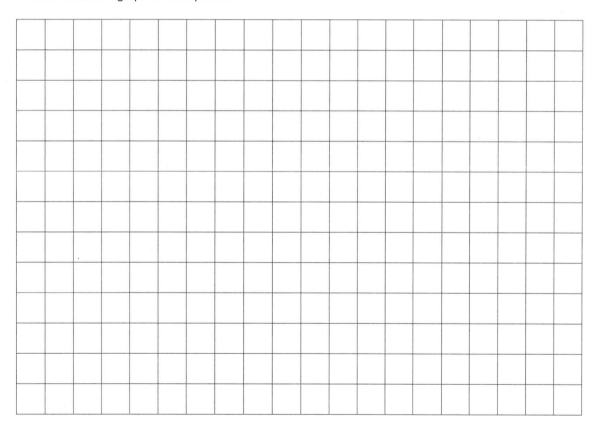

d.   Interpret the points $(0,0)$ and $(1, r)$.

Exercise 5

Use the following table to calculate the markup or markdown rate. Show your work. Is the relationship between the original price and the selling price proportional or not? Explain.

Original Price, m (in dollars)	Selling Price, p (in dollars)
1,750	1,400
1,500	1,200
1,250	1,000
1,000	800
750	600

EUREKA
MATH™

© 2015 Great Minds. eureka-math.org
G7-M3M4-SE-B2-1.3.1-02.2016

Lesson Summary

- To find the final price after a markup or markdown, multiply the whole by $(1 \pm m)$, where m is the markup/markdown rate.

- To apply multiple discount rates to the price of an item, you must find the first discount price and then use this answer to get the second discount price.

Problem Set

1. You have a coupon for an additional 25% off the price of any sale item at a store. The store has put a robotics kit on sale for 15% off the original price of $40. What is the price of the robotics kit after both discounts?

2. A sign says that the price marked on all music equipment is 30% off the original price. You buy an electric guitar for the sale price of $315.

   a. What is the original price?

   b. How much money did you save off the original price of the guitar?

   c. What percent of the original price is the sale price?

3. The cost of a New York Yankee baseball cap is $24.00. The local sporting goods store sells it for $30.00. Find the markup rate.

4. Write an equation to determine the selling price in dollars, p, on an item that is originally priced s dollars after a markdown of 15%.

   a. Create and label a table showing five possible pairs of solutions to the equation.

   b. Create and label a graph of the equation.

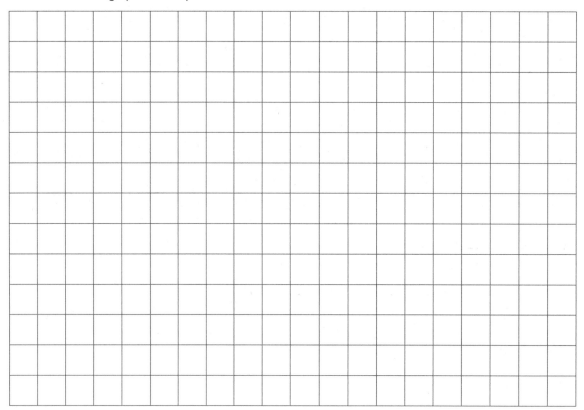

   c. Interpret the points $(0,0)$ and $(1, r)$.

5. At the amusement park, Laura paid $6.00 for a small cotton candy. Her older brother works at the park, and he told her they mark up the cotton candy by 300%. Laura does not think that is mathematically possible. Is it possible, and if so, what is the price of the cotton candy before the markup?

6. A store advertises that customers can take 25% off the original price and then take an extra 10% off. Is this the same as a 35% off discount? Explain.

7. An item that costs $50.00 is marked 20% off. Sales tax for the item is 8%. What is the final price, including tax?

   a. Solve the problem with the discount applied before the sales tax.

   b. Solve the problem with the discount applied after the sales tax.

   c. Compare your answers in parts (a) and (b). Explain.

© 2015 Great Minds. eureka-math.org
G7-M3M4-SE-B2-1.3.1-02.2016

8. The sale price for a bicycle is $315. The original price was first discounted by 50% and then discounted an additional 10%. Find the original price of the bicycle.

9. A ski shop has a markup rate of 50%. Find the selling price of skis that cost the storeowner $300.

10. A tennis supply store pays a wholesaler $90 for a tennis racquet and sells it for $144. What is the markup rate?

11. A shoe store is selling a pair of shoes for $60 that has been discounted by 25%. What was the original selling price?

12. A shoe store has a markup rate of 75% and is selling a pair of shoes for $133. Find the price the store paid for the shoes.

13. Write $5\frac{1}{4}\%$ as a simple fraction.

14. Write $\frac{3}{8}$ as a percent.

15. If 20% of the 70 faculty members at John F. Kennedy Middle School are male, what is the number of male faculty members?

16. If a bag contains 400 coins, and $33\frac{1}{2}\%$ are nickels, how many nickels are there? What percent of the coins are not nickels?

17. The temperature outside is 60 degrees Fahrenheit. What would be the temperature if it is increased by 20%?

This page intentionally left blank

Lesson 8: Percent Error Problems

Example 1: How Far Off?

Student	Measurement 1 (in.)	Measurement 2 (in.)
Taylor	$15\frac{2}{8}$	$15\frac{3}{8}$
Connor	$15\frac{4}{8}$	$14\frac{7}{8}$
Jordan	$15\frac{4}{8}$	$14\frac{6}{8}$

Find the absolute error for the following problems. Explain what the absolute error means in context.

    a.   Taylor's Measurement 1

    b.   Connor's Measurement 1

    c.   Jordan's Measurement 2

© 2015 Great Minds. eureka-math.org
G7-M3M4-SE-B2-1.3.1-02.2016

Example 2: How Right Is Wrong?

a. Find the percent error for Taylor's Measurement 1. What does this mean?

b. From Example 1, part (b), find the percent error for Connor's Measurement 1. What does this mean?

c. From Example 1, part (c), find the percent error for Jordan's Measurement 2. What does it mean?

d. What is the purpose of finding percent error?

© 2015 Great Minds. eureka-math.org
G7-M3M4-SE-B2-1.3.1-02.2016

Exercises

Calculate the percent error for Problems 1–3. Leave your final answer in fraction form, if necessary.

1. A real estate agent expected 18 people to show up for an open house, but 25 attended.

2. In science class, Mrs. Moore's students were directed to weigh a 300-gram mass on the balance scale. Tina weighed the object and reported 328 grams.

3. Darwin's coach recorded that he had bowled 250 points out of 300 in a bowling tournament. However, the official scoreboard showed that Darwin actually bowled 225 points out of 300.

Example 3: Estimating Percent Error

The attendance at a musical event was counted several times. All counts were between 573 and 589. If the actual attendance number is between 573 and 589, inclusive, what is the most the percent error could be? Explain your answer.

© 2015 Great Minds. eureka-math.org
G7-M3M4-SE-B2-1.3.1-02.2016

EUREKA
MATH™

Lesson Summary

- The absolute error is defined as $|a - x|$, where x is the exact value of a quantity and a is an approximate value.

- The percent error is defined as $\frac{|a-x|}{|x|} \times 100\%$.

- The absolute error will tell how big the error is, but the percent error compares the error to the actual value. A good measurement has a small percent error.

Problem Set

1. The odometer in Mr. Washington's car does not work correctly. The odometer recorded 13.2 miles for his last trip to the hardware store, but he knows the distance traveled is 15 miles. What is the percent error? Use a calculator and the percent error formula to help find the answer. Show your steps.

2. The actual length of a soccer field is 500 feet. A measuring instrument shows the length to be 493 feet. The actual width of the field is 250 feet, but the recorded width is 246.5 feet. Answer the following questions based on this information. Round all decimals to the nearest tenth.

    a. Find the percent error for the length of the soccer field.

    b. Find the percent error of the area of the soccer field.

    c. Explain why the values from parts (a) and (b) are different.

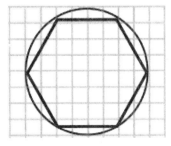

250 feet

500 feet

3. Kayla's class went on a field trip to an aquarium. One tank had 30 clown fish. She miscounted the total number of clown fish in the tank and recorded it as 24 fish. What is Kayla's percent error?

4. Sid used geometry software to draw a circle of radius 4 units on a grid. He estimated the area of the circle by counting the squares that were mostly inside the circle and got an answer of 52 square units.

    a. Is his estimate too large or too small?

    b. Find the percent error in Sid's estimation to the nearest hundredth using the π key on your calculator.

5. The exact value for the density of aluminum is 2.699 g/cm³. Working in the science lab at school, Joseph finds the density of a piece of aluminum to be 2.75 g/cm³. What is Joseph's percent error? (Round to the nearest hundredth.)

6. The world's largest marathon, The New York City Marathon, is held on the first Sunday in November each year. Between 2 million and 2.5 million spectators will line the streets to cheer on the marathon runners. At most, what is the percent error?

7. A circle is inscribed inside a square, which has a side length of 12.6 cm. Jared estimates the area of the circle to be about 80% of the area of the square and comes up with an estimate of 127 cm².

   a. Find the absolute error from Jared's estimate to two decimal places using the π key on your calculator.

   b. Find the percent error of Jared's estimate to two decimal places using the π key on your calculator.

   c. Do you think Jared's estimate was reasonable?

   12.6 cm

   d. Would this method of computing the area of a circle always be too large?

8. In a school library, 52% of the books are paperback. If there are 2,658 books in the library, how many of them are not paperback to the nearest whole number?

9. Shaniqua has 25% less money than her older sister Jennifer. If Shaniqua has $180, how much money does Jennifer have?

10. An item that was selling for $1,102 is reduced to $806. To the nearest whole, what is the percent decrease?

11. If 60 calories from fat is 75% of the total number of calories in a bag of chips, find the total number of calories in the bag of chips.

EUREKA
MATH™

Lesson 9: Problem Solving When the Percent Changes

Classwork

Example 1

The amount of money Tom has is 75% of Sally's amount of money. After Sally spent $120 and Tom saved all his money, Tom's amount of money is 50% more than Sally's. How much money did each have at the beginning? Use a visual model and a percent line to solve the problem.

Example 2

Erin and Sasha went to a candy shop. Sasha bought 50% more candies than Erin. After Erin bought 8 more candies, Sasha had 20% more. How many candies did Erin and Sasha have at first?

    a.   Model the situation using a visual model.

© 2015 Great Minds. eureka-math.org
G7-M3M4-SE-B2-1.3.1-02.2016

b.   How many candies did Erin have at first? Explain.

Example 3

Kimberly and Mike have an equal amount of money. After Kimberly spent $50 and Mike spent $25, Mike's money is 50% more than Kimberly's. How much did Kimberly and Mike have at first?

a.   Use an equation to solve the problem.

b.   Use a visual model to solve the problem.

c.   Which method do you prefer and why?

© 2015 Great Minds. eureka-math.org
G7-M3M4-SE-B2-1.3.1-02.2016

Exercise

Todd has 250% more video games than Jaylon. Todd has 56 video games in his collection. He gives Jaylon 8 of his games. How many video games did Todd and Jaylon have in the beginning? How many do they have now?

Lesson Summary

- To solve a changing percent problem, identify the first whole and then the second whole. To relate the part, whole, and percent, use the formula

  $$\text{Quantity} = \text{Percent} \times \text{Whole}.$$

- Models, such as double number lines, can help visually show the change in quantities and percents.

Problem Set

1. Solve each problem using an equation.
   a. What is 150% of 625?
   b. 90 is 40% of what number?
   c. What percent of 520 is 40? Round to the nearest hundredth of a percent.

2. The actual length of a machine is 12.25 cm. The measured length is 12.2 cm. Round the answer to part (b) to the nearest hundredth of a percent.
   a. Find the absolute error.
   b. Find the percent error.

3. A rowing club has 600 members. 60% of them are women. After 200 new members joined the club, the percentage of women was reduced to 50%. How many of the new members are women?

4. 40% of the marbles in a bag are yellow. The rest are orange and green. The ratio of the number of orange to the number of green is 4:5. If there are 30 green marbles, how many yellow marbles are there? Use a visual model to show your answer.

5. Susan has 50% more books than Michael. Michael has 40 books. If Michael buys 8 more books, will Susan have more or less books than Michael? What percent more or less will Susan's books be? Use any method to solve the problem.

6. Harry's amount of money is 75% of Kayla's amount of money. After Harry earned $30 and Kayla earned 25% more of her money, Harry's amount of money is 80% of Kayla's money. How much money did each have at the beginning? Use a visual model to solve the problem.

© 2015 Great Minds. eureka-math.org
G7-M3M4-SE-B2-1.3.1-02.2016

Lesson 10: Simple Interest

Classwork

To find the simple interest, use the following formula:

$$\text{Interest} = \text{Principal} \times \text{Rate} \times \text{Time}$$

$$I = P \times r \times t$$

$$I = Prt$$

- r is the percent of the principal that is paid over a period of time (usually per year).
- t is the time.
- r and t must be compatible. For example, if r is an annual interst rate, then t must be written in years.

Example 1: Can Money Grow? A Look at Simple Interest

Larry invests $100 in a savings plan. The plan pays $4\frac{1}{2}\%$ interest each year on his $100 account balance.

     a. How much money will Larry earn in interest after 3 years? After 5 years?

     b. How can you find the balance of Larry's account at the end of 5 years?

© 2015 Great Minds. eureka-math.org
G7-M3M4-SE-B2-1.3.1-02.2016

Exercise 1

Find the balance of a savings account at the end of 10 years if the interest earned each year is 7.5%. The principal is $500.

Example 2: Time Other Than One Year

A $1,000 savings bond earns simple interest at the rate of 3% each year. The interest is paid at the end of every month. How much interest will the bond have earned after 3 months?

Example 3: Solving for P, r, or t

Mrs. Williams wants to know how long it will take an investment of $450 to earn $200 in interest if the yearly interest rate is 6.5%, paid at the end of each year.

Exercise 2

Write an equation to find the amount of simple interest, A, earned on a $600 investment after $1\frac{1}{2}$ years if the semi-annual (6-month) interest rate is 2%.

Exercise 3

A $1,500 loan has an annual interest rate of $4\frac{1}{4}$% on the amount borrowed. How much time has elapsed if the interest is now $127.50?

Lesson Summary

- Interest earned over time can be represented by a proportional relationship between time, in years, and interest.
- The simple interest formula is

$$\text{Interest} = \text{Principal} \times \text{Rate} \times \text{Time}$$
$$I = P \times r \times t$$
$$I = Prt$$

  r is the percent of the principal that is paid over a period of time (usually per year).

  t is the time.

- The rate, r, and time, t, must be compatible. If r is the annual interest rate, then t must be written in years.

Problem Set

1. Enrique takes out a student loan to pay for his college tuition this year. Find the interest on the loan if he borrowed $2,500 at an annual interest rate of 6% for 15 years.

2. Your family plans to start a small business in your neighborhood. Your father borrows $10,000 from the bank at an annual interest rate of 8% rate for 36 months. What is the amount of interest he will pay on this loan?

3. Mr. Rodriguez invests $2,000 in a savings plan. The savings account pays an annual interest rate of 5.75% on the amount he put in at the end of each year.

   a. How much will Mr. Rodriguez earn if he leaves his money in the savings plan for 10 years?

   b. How much money will be in his savings plan at the end of 10 years?

   c. Create (and label) a graph in the coordinate plane to show the relationship between time and the amount of interest earned for 10 years. Is the relationship proportional? Why or why not? If so, what is the constant of proportionality?

   d. Explain what the points $(0, 0)$ and $(1, 115)$ mean on the graph.

   e. Using the graph, find the balance of the savings plan at the end of seven years.

   f. After how many years will Mr. Rodriguez have increased his original investment by more than 50%? Show your work to support your answer.

Challenge Problem

4. George went on a game show and won $60,000. He wanted to invest it and found two funds that he liked. Fund 250 earns 15% interest annually, and Fund 100 earns 8% interest annually. George does not want to earn more than $7,500 in interest income this year. He made the table below to show how he could invest the money.

	I	P	r	t
Fund 100		x	0.08	1
Fund 250		$60,000 - x$	0.15	1
Total	7,500	60,000		

a. Explain what value x is in this situation.

b. Explain what the expression $60,000 - x$ represents in this situation.

c. Using the simple interest formula, complete the table for the amount of interest earned.

d. Write an inequality to show the total amount of interest earned from both funds.

e. Use algebraic properties to solve for x and the principal, in dollars, George could invest in Fund 100. Show your work.

f. Use your answer from part (e) to determine how much George could invest in Fund 250.

g. Using your answers to parts (e) and (f), how much interest would George earn from each fund?

This page intentionally left blank

Lesson 11: Tax, Commissions, Fees, and Other Real-World Percent Problems

Classwork

Opening Exercise: Tax, Commission, Gratuity, and Fees

How are each of the following percent applications different, and how are they the same? Solve each problem, and then compare your solution process for each problem.

    a.   Silvio earns 10% for each car sale he makes while working at a used car dealership. If he sells a used car for $2,000, what is his commission?

    b.   Tu's family stayed at a hotel for 10 nights on their vacation. The hotel charged a 10% room tax, per night. How much did they pay in room taxes if the room cost $200 per night?

    c.   Eric bought a new computer and printer online. He had to pay 10% in shipping fees. The items totaled $2,000. How much did the shipping cost?

    d.   Selena had her wedding rehearsal dinner at a restaurant. The restaurant's policy is that gratuity is included in the bill for large parties. Her father said the food and service were exceptional, so he wanted to leave an extra 10% tip on the total amount of the bill. If the dinner bill totaled $2,000, how much money did her father leave as the extra tip?

© 2015 Great Minds. eureka-math.org
G7-M3M4-SE-B2-1.3.1-02.2016

Exercises

Show all work; a calculator may be used for calculations.

The school board has approved the addition of a new sports team at your school.

1. The district ordered 30 team uniforms and received a bill for $2,992.50. The total included a 5% discount.

    a. The school needs to place another order for two more uniforms. The company said the discount will not apply because the discount only applies to orders of $1,000 or more. How much will the two uniforms cost?

    b. The school district does not have to pay the 8% sales tax on the $2,992.50 purchase. Estimate the amount of sales tax the district saved on the $2,992.50 purchase. Explain how you arrived at your estimate.

    c. A student who loses a uniform must pay a fee equal to 75% of the school's cost of the uniform. For a uniform that cost the school $105, will the student owe more or less than $75 for the lost uniform? Explain how to use mental math to determine the answer.

    d. Write an equation to represent the proportional relationship between the school's cost of a uniform and the amount a student must pay for a lost uniform. Use u to represent the uniform cost and s to represent the amount a student must pay for a lost uniform. What is the constant of proportionality?

© 2015 Great Minds. eureka-math.org
G7-M3M4-SE-B2-1.3.1-02.2016

2. A taxpayer claims the new sports team caused his school taxes to increase by 2%.

    a. Write an equation to show the relationship between the school taxes before and after a 2% increase. Use b to represent the dollar amount of school tax before the 2% increase and t to represent the dollar amount of school tax after the 2% increase.

    b. Use your equation to complete the table below, listing at least 5 pairs of values.

b	t
1,000	
2,000	
	3,060
	6,120

    c. On graph paper, graph the relationship modeled by the equation in part (a). Be sure to label the axes and scale.

    d. Is the relationship proportional? Explain how you know.

    e. What is the constant of proportionality? What does it mean in the context of the situation?

    f. If a taxpayers' school taxes rose from $4,000 to $4,020, was there a 2% increase? Justify your answer using your graph, table, or equation.

3. The sports booster club sold candles as a fundraiser to support the new team. The club earns a commission on its candle sales (which means it receives a certain percentage of the total dollar amount sold). If the club gets to keep 30% of the money from the candle sales, what would the club's total sales have to be in order to make at least $500?

4. Christian's mom works at the concession stand during sporting events. She told him they buy candy bars for $0.75 each and mark them up 40% to sell at the concession stand. What is the amount of the markup? How much does the concession stand charge for each candy bar?

EUREKA
MATH

With your group, brainstorm solutions to the problems below. Prepare a poster that shows your solutions and math work. A calculator may be used for calculations.

5. For the next school year, the new soccer team will need to come up with $600.

    a. Suppose the team earns $500 from the fundraiser at the start of the current school year, and the money is placed for one calendar year in a savings account earning 0.5% simple interest annually. How much money will the team still need to raise to meet next year's expenses?

    b. Jeff is a member of the new sports team. His dad owns a bakery. To help raise money for the team, Jeff's dad agrees to provide the team with cookies to sell at the concession stand for next year's opening game. The team must pay back the bakery $0.25 for each cookie it sells. The concession stand usually sells about 60 to 80 baked goods per game. Using your answer from part (a), determine a percent markup for the cookies the team plans to sell at next year's opening game. Justify your answer.

© 2015 Great Minds. eureka-math.org
G7-M3M4-SE-B2-1.3.1-02.2016

c. Suppose the team ends up selling 78 cookies at next year's opening game. Find the percent error in the number of cookies that you estimated would be sold in your solution to part (b).

Percent Error $= \frac{|a-x|}{|x|} \cdot 100\%$, where x is the exact value and a is the approximate value.

EUREKA MATH™

© 2015 Great Minds. eureka-math.org
G7-M3M4-SE-B2-1.3.1-02.2016

Lesson Summary

- There are many real-world problems that involve percents. For example, gratuity (tip), commission, fees, and taxes are applications found daily in the real world. They each increase the total, so all questions like these reflect a percent increase. Likewise, markdowns and discounts decrease the total, so they reflect a percent decrease.

- Regardless of the application, the percent relationship can be represented as

$$\text{Quantity(Part)} = \text{Percent(\%)} \times \text{Whole}$$

Problem Set

1. A school district's property tax rate rises from 2.5% to 2.7% to cover a $300,000 budget deficit (shortage of money). What is the value of the property in the school district to the nearest dollar? (Note: Property is assessed at 100% of its value.)

2. Jake's older brother Sam has a choice of two summer jobs. He can either work at an electronics store or at the school's bus garage. The electronics store would pay him to work 15 hours per week. He would make $8 per hour plus a 2% commission on his electronics sales. At the school's bus garage, Sam could earn $300 per week working 15 hours cleaning buses. Sam wants to take the job that pays him the most. How much in electronics would Sam have to sell for the job at the electronics store to be the better choice for his summer job?

3. Sarah lost her science book. Her school charges a lost book fee equal to 75% of the cost of the book. Sarah received a notice stating she owed the school $60 for the lost book.

   a. Write an equation to represent the proportional relationship between the school's cost for the book and the amount a student must pay for a lost book. Let B represent the school's cost of the book in dollars and N represent the student's cost in dollars.

   b. What is the constant or proportionality? What does it mean in the context of this situation?

   c. How much did the school pay for the book?

Lesson 11:   Tax, Commissions, Fees, and Other Real-World Percent Problems   S.75

© 2015 Great Minds. eureka-math.org
G7-M3M4-SE-B2-1.3.1-02.2016

4. In the month of May, a certain middle school has an average daily absentee rate of 8% each school day. The absentee rate is the percent of students who are absent from school each day.

    a. Write an equation that shows the proportional relationship between the number of students enrolled in the middle school and the average number of students absent each day during the month of May. Let s represent the number of students enrolled in school, and let a represent the average number of students absent each day in May.

    b. Use your equation to complete the table. List 5 possible values for s and a.

s	a

    c. Identify the constant of proportionality, and explain what it means in the context of this situation.

    d. Based on the absentee rate, determine the number of students absent on average from school during the month of May if there are 350 students enrolled in the middle school.

5. The equation shown in the box below could relate to many different percent problems. Put an X next to each problem that could be represented by this equation. For any problem that does not match this equation, explain why it does not. $\boxed{\text{Quantity} = 1.05 \cdot \text{Whole}}$

    _____   Find the amount of an investment after 1 year with 0.5% interest paid annually.

    _____   Write an equation to show the amount paid for an item including tax, if the tax rate is 5%.

    _____   A proportional relationship has a constant of proportionality equal to 105%.

Whole	0	100	200	300	400	500
Quantity	0	105	210	315	420	525

    _____   Mr. Hendrickson sells cars and earns a 5% commission on every car he sells. Write an equation to show the relationship between the price of a car Mr. Hendrickson sold and the amount of commission he earns.

© 2015 Great Minds. eureka-math.org
G7-M3M4-SE-B2-1.3.1-02.2016

Lesson 12: The Scale Factor as a Percent for a Scale Drawing

Opening

Compare the corresponding lengths of Figure A to the original octagon in the middle. This is an example of a particular type of *scale drawing* called a

_____. Explain why it is called that.

Compare the corresponding lengths of Figure B to the original octagon in the middle. This is an example of a particular type of *scale drawing* called an

_____. Explain why it is called that.

The *scale factor* is the quotient of any length in the scale drawing to its corresponding length in the actual drawing.

Use what you recall from Module 1 to determine the scale factors between the original figure and Figure A and the original figure and Figure B.

Use the diagram to complete the chart below to determine the horizontal and vertical scale factors. Write answers as a percent and as a concluding statement using the previously learned reduction and enlargement vocabulary.

	Horizontal Measurement in Scale Drawing	Vertical Measurement in Scale Drawing	Concluding Statement
Figure A			
Figure B			

Example 1

Create a snowman on the accompanying grid. Use the octagon given as the middle of the snowman with the following conditions:

a. Calculate the width, neck, and height, in units, for the figure to the right.

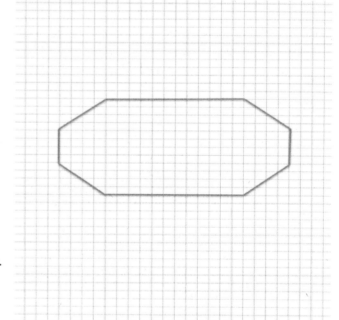

b. To create the head of the snowman, make a scale drawing of the middle of the snowman with a scale factor of 75%. Calculate the new lengths, in units, for the width, neck, and height.

c. To create the bottom of the snowman, make a scale drawing of the middle of the snowman with a scale factor of 125%. Calculate the new lengths, in units, for the width, waist, and height.

d. Is the head a reduction or enlargement of the middle?

e. Is the bottom a reduction or enlargement of the middle?

f. What is the significance of the scale factor as it relates to 100%? What happens when such scale factors are applied?

g. Use the dimensions you calculated in parts (b) and (c) to draw the complete snowman.

Example 2

Create a scale drawing of the arrow below using a scale factor of 150%.

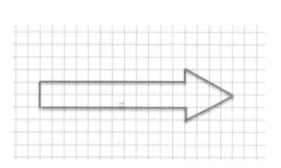 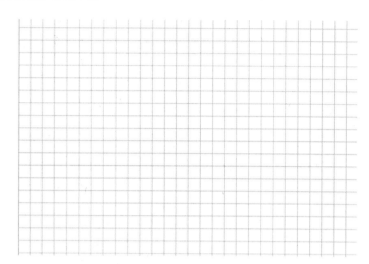

Example 3: Scale Drawings Where the Horizontal and Vertical Scale Factors Are Different

Sometimes it is helpful to make a scale drawing where the horizontal and vertical scale factors are different, such as when creating diagrams in the field of engineering. Having differing scale factors may distort some drawings. For example, when you are working with a very large horizontal scale, you sometimes must exaggerate the vertical scale in order to make it readable. This can be accomplished by creating a drawing with two scales. Unlike the scale drawings with just one scale factor, these types of scale drawings may look distorted. Next to the drawing below is a scale drawing with a horizontal scale factor of 50% and vertical scale factor of 25% (given in two steps). Explain how each drawing is created.

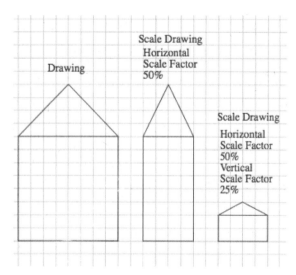

           The Scale Factor as a Percent for a Scale Drawing

EUREKA MATH

© 2015 Great Minds. eureka-math.org
G7-M3M4-SE-B2-1.3.1-02.2016

Exercise 1

Create a scale drawing of the following drawing using a horizontal scale factor of $183\frac{1}{3}\%$ and a vertical scale factor of 25%.

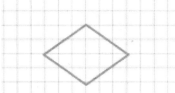

Exercise 2

Chris is building a rectangular pen for his dog. The dimensions are 12 units long and 5 units wide.

12 Units

5 Units

Chris is building a second pen that is 60% the length of the original and 125% the width of the original. Write equations to determine the length and width of the second pen.

Problem Set

1. Use the diagram below to create a scale drawing using a scale factor of $133\frac{1}{3}\%$. Write numerical equations to find the horizontal and vertical distances in the scale drawing.

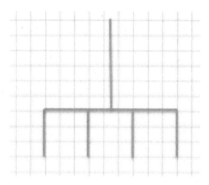

2. Create a scale drawing of the original drawing given below using a horizontal scale factor of 80% and a vertical scale factor of 175%. Write numerical equations to find the horizontal and vertical distances.

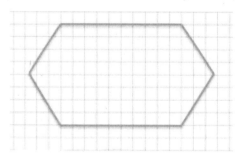

EUREKA
MATH™

3. The accompanying diagram shows that the length of a pencil from its eraser to its tip is 7 units and that the eraser is 1.5 units wide. The picture was placed on a photocopy machine and reduced to $66\frac{2}{3}\%$. Find the new size of the pencil, and sketch a drawing. Write numerical equations to find the new dimensions.

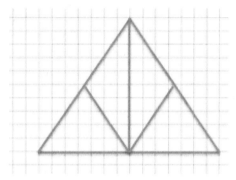

1.5 units

----------------------7 units-----------------------

4. Use the diagram to answer each question.
   a. What are the corresponding horizontal and vertical distances in a scale drawing if the scale factor is 25%? Use numerical equations to find your answers.

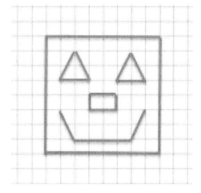

   b. What are the corresponding horizontal and vertical distances in a scale drawing if the scale factor is 160%? Use a numerical equation to find your answers.

5. Create a scale drawing of the original drawing below using a horizontal scale factor of 200% and a vertical scale factor of 250%.

6. Using the diagram below, on grid paper sketch the same drawing using a horizontal scale factor of 50% and a vertical scale factor of 150%.

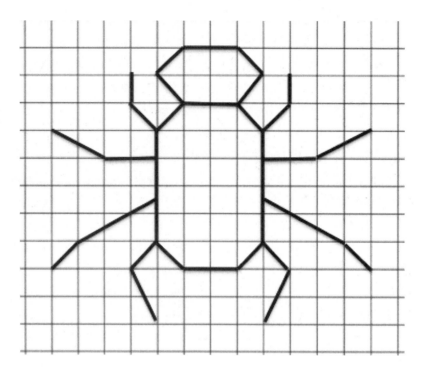

Lesson 12:   The Scale Factor as a Percent for a Scale Drawing

EUREKA
MATH™

© 2015 Great Minds. eureka-math.org
G7-M3M4-SE-B2-1.3.1-02.2016

Lesson 13: Changing Scales

Opening Exercise

$$\text{Scale factor:} \quad \frac{\text{length in SCALE drawing}}{\text{Corresponding length in ORIGINAL drawing}}$$

Describe, using percentages, the difference between a reduction and an enlargement.

Use the two drawings below to complete the chart. Calculate the first row (Drawing 1 to Drawing 2) only.

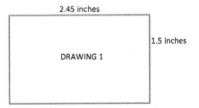

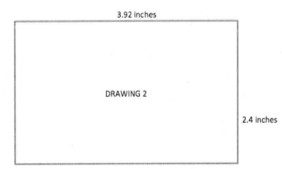

	Quotient of Corresponding Horizontal Distances	Quotient of Corresponding Vertical Distances	Scale Factor as a Percent	Reduction or Enlargement?
Drawing 1 to Drawing 2				
Drawing 2 to Drawing 1				

Compare Drawing 2 to Drawing 1. Using the completed work in the first row, make a conjecture (statement) about what the second row of the chart will be. Justify your conjecture without computing the second row.

Compute the second row of the chart. Was your conjecture proven true? Explain how you know.

Example 1

The scale factor from Drawing 1 to Drawing 2 is 60%. Find the scale factor from Drawing 2 to Drawing 1. Explain your reasoning.

Example 2

A regular octagon is an eight-sided polygon with side lengths that are all equal. All three octagons are scale drawings of each other. Use the chart and the side lengths to compute each scale factor as a percent. How can we check our answers?

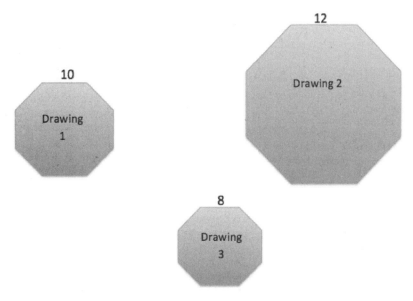

Actual Drawing to Scale Drawing	Scale Factor	Equation to Illustrate Relationship
Drawing 1 to Drawing 2		
Drawing 1 to Drawing 3		
Drawing 2 to Drawing 1		

Drawing 2 to Drawing 3		
Drawing 3 to Drawing 1		
Drawing 3 to Drawing 2		

Lesson 13: Changing Scales

EUREKA MATH

Example 3

The scale factor from Drawing 1 to Drawing 2 is 112%, and the scale factor from Drawing 1 to Drawing 3 is 84%. Drawing 2 is also a scale drawing of Drawing 3. Is Drawing 2 a reduction or an enlargement of Drawing 3? Justify your answer using the scale factor. The drawing is not necessarily drawn to scale.

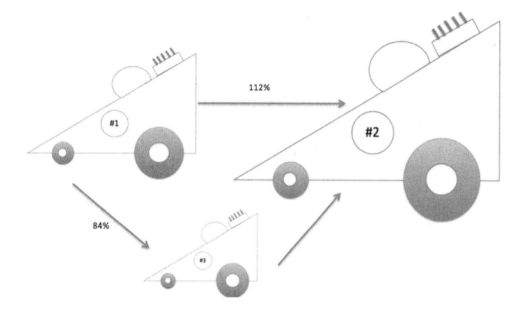

Explain how you could use the scale factors from Drawing 1 to Drawing 2 (112%) and from Drawing 2 to Drawing 3 (75%) to show that the scale factor from Drawing 1 to Drawing 3 is 84%.

Lesson Summary

To compute the scale factor from one drawing to another, use the representation:

Quantity = Percent × Whole

where the whole is the length in the actual or original drawing and the quantity is the length in the scale drawing.

If the lengths of the sides are not provided but two scale factors are provided, use the same relationship but use the scale factors as the whole and quantity instead of the given measurements.

Problem Set

1. The scale factor from Drawing 1 to Drawing 2 is $41\frac{2}{3}\%$. Justify why Drawing 1 is a scale drawing of Drawing 2 and why it is an enlargement of Drawing 2. Include the scale factor in your justification.

2. The scale factor from Drawing 1 to Drawing 2 is 40%, and the scale factor from Drawing 2 to Drawing 3 is 37.5%. What is the scale factor from Drawing 1 to Drawing 3? Explain your reasoning, and check your answer using an example.

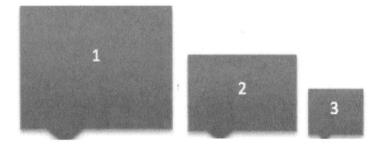

EUREKA MATH

3. Traci took a photograph and printed it to be a size of 4 units by 4 units as indicated in the diagram. She wanted to enlarge the original photograph to a size of 5 units by 5 units and 10 units by 10 units.

   a. Sketch the different sizes of photographs.

   4

   b. What was the scale factor from the original photo to the photo that is 5 units by 5 units?

   c. What was the scale factor from the original photo to the photo that is 10 units by 10 units?

   d. What was the scale factor from the 5×5 photo to the 10×10 photo?

   e. Write an equation to verify how the scale factor from the original photo to the enlarged 10×10 photo can be calculated using the scale factors from the original to the 5×5, and then from the 5×5 to the 10×10.

4. The scale factor from Drawing 1 to Drawing 2 is 30%, and the scale factor from Drawing 1 to Drawing 3 is 175%. What are the scale factors of each given relationship? Then, answer the question that follows. Drawings are not to scale.

   a. Drawing 2 to Drawing 3

   b. Drawing 3 to Drawing 1

   c. Drawing 3 to Drawing 2

   d. How can you check your answers?

   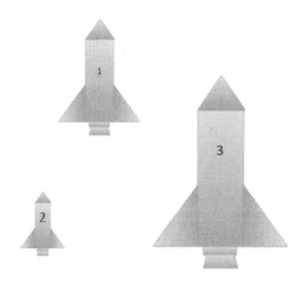

This page intentionally left blank

Lesson 14: Computing Actual Lengths from a Scale Drawing

Classwork

Example 1

The distance around the entire small boat is 28.4 units. The larger figure is a scale drawing of the smaller drawing of the boat. State the scale factor as a percent, and then use the scale factor to find the distance around the scale drawing.

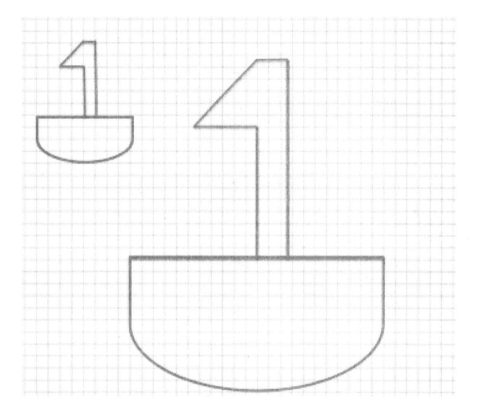

Exercise 1

The length of the longer path is 32.4 units. The shorter path is a scale drawing of the longer path. Find the length of the shorter path, and explain how you arrived at your answer.

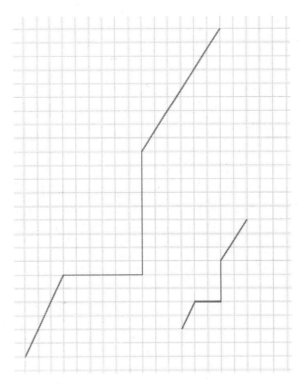

Lesson 14:   Computing Actual Lengths from a Scale Drawing

EUREKA
MATH™

Example 2: Time to Garden

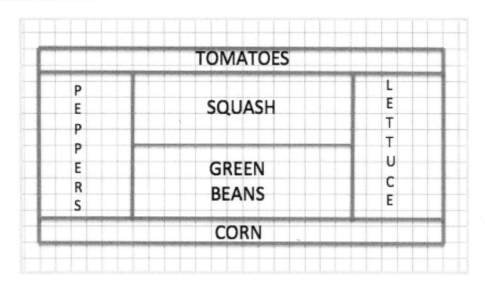

Sherry designed her garden as shown in the diagram above. The distance between any two consecutive vertical grid lines is 1 foot, and the distance between any two consecutive horizontal grid lines is also 1 foot. Therefore, each grid square has an area of one square foot. After designing the garden, Sherry decided to actually build the garden 75% of the size represented in the diagram.

a. What are the outside dimensions shown in the blueprint?

b. What will the overall dimensions be in the actual garden? Write an equation to find the dimensions. How does the problem relate to the scale factor?

c. If Sherry plans to use a wire fence to divide each section of the garden, how much fence does she need?

d. If the fence costs $3.25 per foot plus 7% sales tax, how much would the fence cost in total?

Lesson 14:   Computing Actual Lengths from a Scale Drawing

EUREKA
MATH™

© 2015 Great Minds. eureka-math.org
G7-M3M4-SE-B2-1.3.1-02.2016

Example 3

Race Car #2 is a scale drawing of Race Car #1. The measurement from the front of Race Car #1 to the back of Race Car #1 is 12 feet, while the measurement from the front of Race Car #2 to the back of Race Car #2 is 39 feet. If the height of Race Car #1 is 4 feet, find the scale factor, and write an equation to find the height of Race Car #2. Explain what each part of the equation represents in the situation.

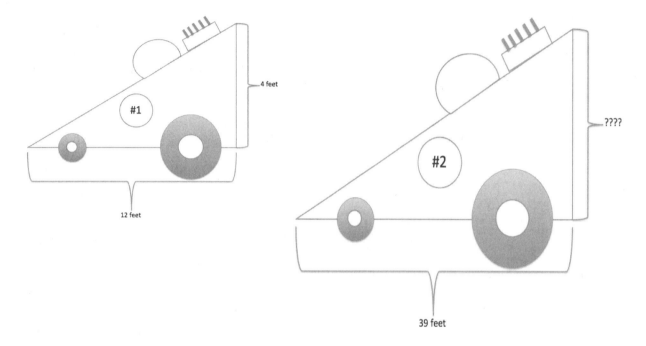

Exercise 2

Determine the scale factor, and write an equation that relates the height of side A in Drawing 1 and the height of side B in Drawing 2 to the scale factor. The height of side A is 1.1 cm. Explain how the equation illustrates the relationship.

2 cm

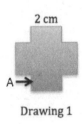

A→

Drawing 1

3.3 cm

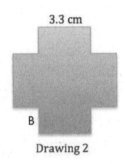

B

Drawing 2

Exercise 3

The length of a rectangular picture is 8 inches, and the picture is to be reduced to be $45\frac{1}{2}\%$ of the original picture. Write an equation that relates the lengths of each picture. Explain how the equation illustrates the relationship.

© 2015 Great Minds. eureka-math.org
G7-M3M4-SE-B2-1.3.1-02.2016

Lesson Summary

The scale factor is the number that determines whether the new drawing is an enlargement or a reduction of the original. If the scale factor is greater than 100%, then the resulting drawing is an enlargement of the original drawing. If the scale factor is less than 100%, then the resulting drawing is a reduction of the original drawing.

To compute actual lengths from a scale drawing, a scale factor must first be determined. To do this, use the relationship Quantity = Percent × Whole, where the original drawing represents the whole and the scale drawing represents the quantity. Once a scale factor is determined, then the relationship Quantity = Percent × Whole can be used again using the scale factor as the percent, the actual length from the original drawing as the whole, and the actual length of the scale drawing as the quantity.

Problem Set

1. The smaller train is a scale drawing of the larger train. If the length of the tire rod connecting the three tires of the larger train, as shown below, is 36 inches, write an equation to find the length of the tire rod of the smaller train. Interpret your solution in the context of the problem.

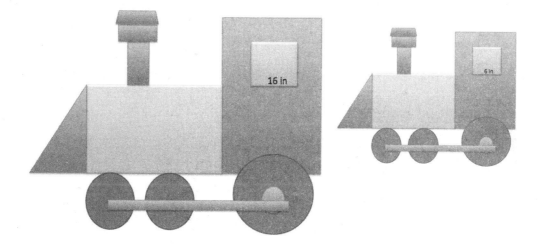

2. The larger arrow is a scale drawing of the smaller arrow. The distance around the smaller arrow is 25.66 units. What is the distance around the larger arrow? Use an equation to find the distance and interpret your solution in the context of the problem.

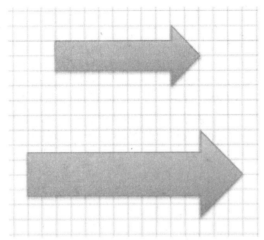

3. The smaller drawing below is a scale drawing of the larger. The distance around the larger drawing is 39.4 units. Using an equation, find the distance around the smaller drawing.

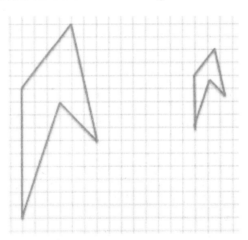

4. The figure is a diagram of a model rocket and is a two-dimensional scale drawing of an actual rocket. The length of a model rocket is 2.5 feet, and the wing span is 1.25 feet. If the length of an actual rocket is 184 feet, use an equation to find the wing span of the actual rocket.

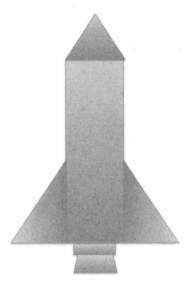

EUREKA
MATH™

Lesson 15: Solving Area Problems Using Scale Drawings

Classwork

Opening Exercise

For each diagram, Drawing 2 is a scale drawing of Drawing 1. Complete the accompanying charts. For each drawing, identify the side lengths, determine the area, and compute the scale factor. Convert each scale factor into a fraction and percent, examine the results, and write a conclusion relating scale factors to area.

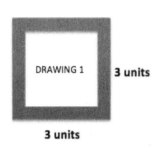

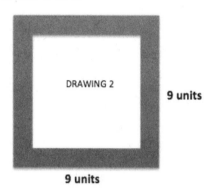

	Drawing 1	Drawing 2	Scale Factor as a Fraction and Percent
Side			
Area (sq. units)			

Scale Factor: _____   Quotient of Areas: _____

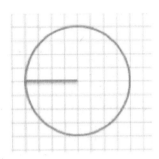

DRAWING 1

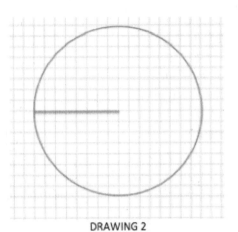

DRAWING 2

	Drawing 1	Drawing 2	Scale Factor as a Fraction and Percent
Radius			
Area (sq. units)			

Scale Factor: _____   Quotient of Areas: _____

The length of each side in Drawing 1 is 12 units, and the length of each side in Drawing 2 is 6 units.

Drawing 1

Drawing 2

	Drawing 1	Drawing 2	Scale Factor as a Fraction and Percent
Side			
Area (sq. units)			

Scale Factor: _____   Quotient of Areas: _____

Conclusion:

Example 1

What percent of the area of the large square is the area of the small square?

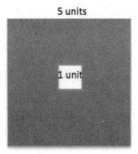

Example 2

What percent of the area of the large disk lies outside the shaded disk?

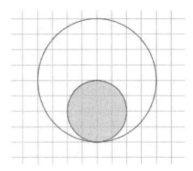

Example 3

If the area of the shaded region in the larger figure is approximately 21.5 square inches, write an equation that relates the areas using scale factor and explain what each quantity represents. Determine the area of the shaded region in the smaller scale drawing.

10 inches

6 inches

EUREKA
MATH

Example 4

Use Figure 1 below and the enlarged scale drawing to justify why the area of the scale drawing is k^2 times the area of the original figure.

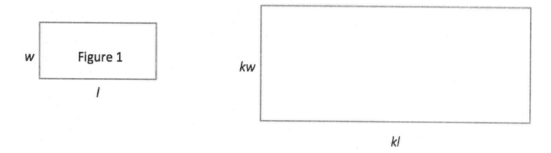

Explain why the expressions $(kl)(kw)$ and $k^2 lw$ are equivalent. How do the expressions reveal different information about this situation?

Exercise 1

The Lake Smith basketball team had a team picture taken of the players, the coaches, and the trophies from the season. The picture was 4 inches by 6 inches. The team decided to have the picture enlarged to a poster and then enlarged again to a banner measuring 48 inches by 72 inches.

    a.   Sketch drawings to illustrate the original picture and enlargements.

© 2015 Great Minds. eureka-math.org
G7-M3M4-SE-B2-1.3.1-02.2016

b.   If the scale factor from the picture to the poster is 500%, determine the dimensions of the poster.

c.   What scale factor is used to create the banner from the picture?

d.   What percent of the area of the picture is the area of the poster? Justify your answer using the scale factor and by finding the actual areas.

© 2015 Great Minds. eureka-math.org
G7-M3M4-SE-B2-1.3.1-02.2016

e.   Write an equation involving the scale factor that relates the area of the poster to the area of the picture.

f.   Assume you started with the banner and wanted to reduce it to the size of the poster. What would the scale factor as a percent be?

g.   What scale factor would be used to reduce the poster to the size of the picture?

Lesson Summary

If the scale factor is represented by k, then the area of the scale drawing is k^2 times the corresponding area of the original drawing.

Problem Set

1. What percent of the area of the larger circle is shaded?

    a. Solve this problem using scale factors.

    b. Verify your work in part (a) by finding the actual areas.

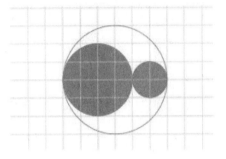

2. The area of the large disk is 50.24 units^2.

    a. Find the area of the shaded region using scale factors. Use 3.14 as an estimate for π.

    b. What percent of the large circular region is unshaded?

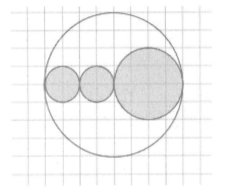

3. Ben cut the following rockets out of cardboard. The height from the base to the tip of the smaller rocket is 20 cm. The height from the base to the tip of the larger rocket is 120 cm. What percent of the area of the smaller rocket is the area of the larger rocket?

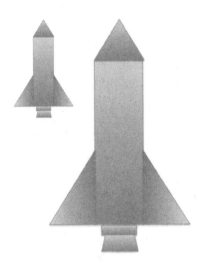

Lesson 15:   Solving Area Problems Using Scale Drawings

EUREKA MATH

4. In the photo frame depicted below, three 5 inch by 5 inch squares are cut out for photographs. If these cut-out regions make up $\frac{3}{16}$ of the area of the entire photo frame, what are the dimensions of the photo frame?

5. Kelly was online shopping for envelopes for party invitations and saw these images on a website.

The website listed the dimensions of the small envelope as 6 in. by 8 in. and the medium envelope as 10 in. by $13\frac{1}{3}$ in.

a. Compare the dimensions of the small and medium envelopes. If the medium envelope is a scale drawing of the small envelope, what is the scale factor?

b. If the large envelope was created based on the dimensions of the small envelope using a scale factor of 250%, find the dimensions of the large envelope.

c. If the medium envelope was created based on the dimensions of the large envelope, what scale factor was used to create the medium envelope?

d. What percent of the area of the larger envelope is the area of the medium envelope?

This page intentionally left blank

Lesson 16: Population Problems

Classwork

Opening Exercise

Number of girls in classroom:	Number of boys in classroom:	Total number of students in classroom:
Percent of the total number of students that are girls:	Percent of the total number of students that are boys:	Percent of boys and girls in the classroom:
Number of girls whose names start with a vowel:	Number of boys whose names start with a vowel:	Number of students whose names start with a vowel:
Percent of girls whose names start with a vowel:	Percent of boys whose names start with a vowel:	
Percent of the total number of students who are girls whose names start with a vowel:	Percent of the total number of students who are boys whose names start with a vowel:	Percent of students whose names start with a vowel:

Example 1

A school has 60% girls and 40% boys. If 20% of the girls wear glasses and 40% of the boys wear glasses, what percent of all students wears glasses?

Exercise 1

How does the percent of students who wear glasses change if the percent of girls and boys remains the same (that is, 60% girls and 40% boys), but 20% of the boys wear glasses and 40% of the girls wear glasses?

EUREKA
MATH™

Lesson 16:   Population Problems

S.113

© 2015 Great Minds. eureka-math.org
G7-M3M4-SE-B2-1.3.1-02.2016

Exercise 2

How would the percent of students who wear glasses change if the percent of girls is 40% of the school and the percent of boys is 60% of the school, and 40% of the girls wear glasses and 20% of the boys wear glasses? Why?

Example 2

The weight of the first three containers is 12% more than the second, and the third container is 20% lighter than the second. By what percent is the first container heavier than the third container?

Exercise 3

Matthew's pet dog is 7% heavier than Harrison's pet dog, and Janice's pet dog is 20% lighter than Harrison's. By what percent is Matthew's dog heavier than Janice's?

Example 3

In one year's time, 20% of Ms. McElroy's investments increased by 5%, 30% of her investments decreased by 5%, and 50% of her investments increased by 3%. By what percent did the total of her investments increase?

EUREKA
MATH™

© 2015 Great Minds. eureka-math.org
G7-M3M4-SE-B2-1.3.1-02.2016

Exercise 4

A concert had 6,000 audience members in attendance on the first night and the same on the second night. On the first night, the concert exceeded expected attendance by 20%, while the second night was below the expected attendance by 20%. What was the difference in percent of concert attendees and expected attendees for both nights combined?

Lesson Summary

When solving a percent population problem, you must first define the variable. This gives a reference of what the whole is. Then, multiply the sub-populations (such as girls and boys) by the given category (total students wearing glasses) to find the percent in the whole population.

Problem Set

1. One container is filled with a mixture that is 30% acid. A second container is filled with a mixture that is 50% acid. The second container is 50% larger than the first, and the two containers are emptied into a third container. What percent of acid is in the third container?

2. The store's markup on a wholesale item is 40%. The store is currently having a sale, and the item sells for 25% off the retail price. What is the percent of profit made by the store?

3. During lunch hour at a local restaurant, 90% of customers order a meat entrée and 10% order a vegetarian entrée. Of the customers who order a meat entrée, 80% order a drink. Of the customers who order a vegetarian entrée, 40% order a drink. What is the percent of customers who order a drink with their entrée?

4. Last year's spell-a-thon spelling test for a first grade class had 15% more words with four or more letters than this year's spelling test. Next year, there will be 5% less than this year. What percent more words have four or more letters in last year's test than next year's?

5. An ice cream shop sells 75% less ice cream in December than in June. Twenty percent more ice cream is sold in July than in June. By what percent did ice cream sales increase from December to July?

6. The livestock on a small farm the prior year consisted of 40% goats, 10% cows, and 50% chickens. This year, there is a 5% decrease in goats, 9% increase in cows, and 15% increase in chickens. What is the percent increase or decrease of livestock this year?

7. In a pet shelter that is occupied by 55% dogs and 45% cats, 60% of the animals are brought in by concerned people who found these animals in the streets. If 90% of the dogs are brought in by concerned people, what is the percent of cats that are brought in by concerned people?

8. An artist wants to make a particular teal color paint by mixing a 75% blue hue and 25% yellow hue. He mixes a blue hue that has 85% pure blue pigment and a yellow hue that has 60% of pure yellow pigment. What is the percent of pure pigment that is in the resulting teal color paint?

9. On Mina's block, 65% of her neighbors do not have any pets, and 35% of her neighbors own at least one pet. If 25% of the neighbors have children but no pets, and 60% of the neighbors who have pets also have children, what percent of the neighbors have children?

Lesson 17: Mixture Problems

Classwork

Opening Exercise

Imagine you have two equally-sized containers. One is pure water, and the other is 50% water and 50% juice. If you combined them, what percent of juice would be the result?

	1st Liquid	2nd Liquid	Resulting Liquid
Amount of Liquid (gallons)			
Amount of Pure Juice (gallons)			

If a 2-gallon container of pure juice is added to 3 gallons of water, what percent of the mixture is pure juice?

	1st Liquid	2nd Liquid	Resulting Liquid
Amount of Liquid (gallons)			
Amount of Pure Juice (gallons)			

If a 2-gallon container of juice mixture that is 40% pure juice is added to 3 gallons of water, what percent of the mixture is pure juice?

	1st Liquid	2nd Liquid	Resulting Liquid
Amount of Liquid (gallons)			
Amount of Pure Juice (gallons)			

If a 2-gallon juice cocktail that is 40% pure juice is added to 3 gallons of pure juice, what percent of the resulting mixture is pure juice?

	1st Liquid	2nd Liquid	Resulting Liquid
Amount of Liquid (gallons)			
Amount of Pure Juice (gallons)			

Example 1

A 5-gallon container of trail mix is 20% nuts. Another trail mix is added to it, resulting in a 12-gallon container of trail mix that is 40% nuts.

a. Write an equation to describe the relationships in this situation.

b. Explain in words how each part of the equation relates to the situation.

c. What percent of the second trail mix is nuts?

© 2015 Great Minds. eureka-math.org
G7-M3M4-SE-B2-1.3.1-02.2016

Exercise 1

Represent each situation using an equation, and show all steps in the solution process.

a.   A 6-pint mixture that is 25% oil is added to a 3-pint mixture that is 40% oil. What percent of the resulting mixture is oil?

b.   An 11-ounce gold chain of 24% gold was made from a melted down 4-ounce charm of 50% gold and a golden locket. What percent of the locket was pure gold?

c.   In a science lab, two containers are filled with mixtures. The first container is filled with a mixture that is 30% acid. The second container is filled with a mixture that is 50% acid, and the second container is 50% larger than the first. The first and second containers are then emptied into a third container. What percent of acid is in the third container?

Example 2

Soil that contains 30% clay is added to soil that contains 70% clay to create 10 gallons of soil containing 50% clay. How much of each of the soils was combined?

Exercise 2

The equation $(0.2)(x) + (0.8)(6 - x) = (0.4)(6)$ is used to model a mixture problem.

a. How many units are in the total mixture?

b. What percents relate to the two solutions that are combined to make the final mixture?

c. The two solutions combine to make 6 units of what percent solution?

d. When the amount of a resulting solution is given (for instance, 4 gallons) but the amounts of the mixing solutions are unknown, how are the amounts of the mixing solutions represented?

EUREKA
MATH

Lesson Summary

- Mixture problems deal with quantities of solutions and mixtures.
- The general structure of the expressions for mixture problems are

$$\text{Whole Quantity} = \text{Part} + \text{Part}.$$

- Using this structure makes the equation resemble the following:

$$(\%\ \text{of resulting quantity})(\text{amount of resulting quantity}) =$$
$$(\%\ \text{of 1}^{\text{st}}\ \text{quantity})(\text{amount of 1}^{\text{st}}\ \text{quantity}) + (\%\ \text{of 2}^{\text{nd}}\ \text{quantity})(\text{amount of 2}^{\text{nd}}\ \text{quantity}).$$

Problem Set

1. A 5-liter cleaning solution contains 30% bleach. A 3-liter cleaning solution contains 50% bleach. What percent of bleach is obtained by putting the two mixtures together?

2. A container is filled with 100 grams of bird feed that is 80% seed. How many grams of bird feed containing 5% seed must be added to get bird feed that is 40% seed?

3. A container is filled with 100 grams of bird feed that is 80% seed. Tom and Sally want to mix the 100 grams with bird feed that is 5% seed to get a mixture that is 40% seed. Tom wants to add 114 grams of the 5% seed, and Sally wants to add 115 grams of the 5% seed mix. What will be the percent of seed if Tom adds 114 grams? What will be the percent of seed if Sally adds 115 grams? How much do you think should be added to get 40% seed?

4. Jeanie likes mixing leftover salad dressings together to make new dressings. She combined 0.55 L of a 90% vinegar salad dressing with 0.45 L of another dressing to make 1 L of salad dressing that is 60% vinegar. What percent of the second salad dressing was vinegar?

5. Anna wants to make 30 mL of a 60% salt solution by mixing together a 72% salt solution and a 54% salt solution. How much of each solution must she use?

6. A mixed bag of candy is 25% chocolate bars and 75% other filler candy. Of the chocolate bars, 50% of them contains caramel. Of the other filler candy, 10% of them contain caramel. What percent of candy contains caramel?

7. A local fish market receives the daily catch of two local fishermen. The first fisherman's catch was 84% fish while the rest was other non-fish items. The second fisherman's catch was 76% fish while the rest was other non-fish items. If the fish market receives 75% of its catch from the first fisherman and 25% from the second, what was the percent of other non-fish items the local fish market bought from the fishermen altogether?

This page intentionally left blank

Lesson 18: Counting Problems

Opening Exercise

You are about to switch out your books from your locker during passing period but forget the order of your locker combination. You know that there are the numbers 3, 16, and 21 in some order. What is the percent of locker combinations that start with 3?

Locker Combination Possibilities:

3, 16, 21

21, 16, 3

16, 21, 3

21, 3, 16

16, 3, 21

3, 21, 16

Example 1

All of the 3-letter passwords that can be formed using the letters A and B are as follows: AAA, AAB, ABA, ABB, BAA, BAB, BBA, BBB.

a.   What percent of passwords contain at least two B's?

b.   What percent of passwords contain no A's?

Exercises 1–2

1. How many 4-letter passwords can be formed using the letters A and B?

2. What percent of the 4-letter passwords contain

    a. No A's?

    b. Exactly one A?

    c. Exactly two A's?

    d. Exactly three A's?

    e. Four A's?

    f. The same number of A's and B's?

Example 2

In a set of 3-letter passwords, 40% of the passwords contain the letter B and two of another letter. Which of the two sets below meets the criteria? Explain how you arrived at your answer.

	Set 1	
BBB	AAA	CAC
CBC	ABA	CCC
BBC	CCB	CAB
AAB	AAC	BAA
ACB	BAC	BCC

	Set 2
CEB	BBB
EBE	CCC
CCC	EEE
EEB	CBC
CCB	ECE

Exercises 3–4

3. Shana read the following problem:

    "How many letter arrangements can be formed from the word *triangle* that have two vowels and two consonants (order does not matter)?"

    She answered that there are 30 letter arrangements.

    Twenty percent of the letter arrangements that began with a vowel actually had an English definition. How many letter arrangements that begin with a vowel have an English definition?

4. Using three different keys on a piano, a songwriter makes the beginning of his melody with three notes, C, E, and G:
    CCE, EEE, EGC, GCE, CEG, GEE, CGE, GGE, EGG, EGE, GCG, EEC, ECC, ECG, GGG, GEC, CCG, CEE, CCC, GEG, CGC.

    a. From the list above, what is the percent of melodies with all three notes that are different?

    b. From the list above, what is the percent of melodies that have three of the same notes?

Example 3

Look at the 36 points on the coordinate plane with whole number coordinates between 1 and 6, inclusive.

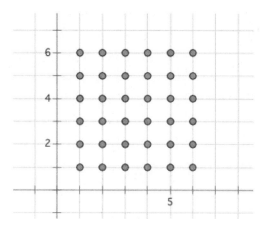

a. Draw a line through each of the points which have an x-coordinate and y-coordinate sum of 7.
    Draw a line through each of the points which have an x-coordinate and y-coordinate sum of 6.
    Draw a line through each of the points which have an x-coordinate and y-coordinate sum of 5.
    Draw a line through each of the points which have an x-coordinate and y-coordinate sum of 4.
    Draw a line through each of the points which have an x-coordinate and y-coordinate sum of 3.
    Draw a line through each of the points which have an x-coordinate and y-coordinate sum of 2.
    Draw a line through each of the points which have an x-coordinate and y-coordinate sum of 8.
    Draw a line through each of the points which have an x-coordinate and y-coordinate sum of 9.
    Draw a line through each of the points which have an x-coordinate and y-coordinate sum of 10.
    Draw a line through each of the points which have an x-coordinate and y-coordinate sum of 11.
    Draw a line through each of the points which have an x-coordinate and y-coordinate sum of 12.

EUREKA
MATH™

b.   What percent of the 36 points have coordinate sum 7?

c.   Write a numerical expression that could be used to determine the percent of the 36 points that have a coordinate sum of 7.

d.   What percent of the 36 points have coordinate sum 5 or less?

e.   What percent of the 36 points have coordinate sum 4 or 10?

© 2015 Great Minds. eureka-math.org
G7-M3M4-SE-B2-1.3.1-02.2016

Lesson Summary

To find the percent of possible outcomes for a counting problem you need to determine the total number of possible outcomes and the different favorable outcomes. The representation

$$\text{Quantity} = \text{Percent} \times \text{Whole}$$

can be used where the quantity is the number of different favorable outcomes and the whole is the total number of possible outcomes.

Problem Set

1. A six-sided die (singular for dice) is thrown twice. The different rolls are as follows:

    1 and 1, 1 and 2, 1 and 3, 1 and 4, 1 and 5, 1 and 6,
    2 and 1, 2 and 2, 2 and 3, 2 and 4, 2 and 5, 2 and 6,
    3 and 1, 3 and 2, 3 and 3, 3 and 4, 3 and 5, 3 and 6,
    4 and 1, 4 and 2, 4 and 3, 4 and 4, 4 and 5, 4 and 6,
    5 and 1, 5 and 2, 5 and 3, 5 and 4, 5 and 5, 5 and 6,
    6 and 1, 6 and 2, 6 and 3, 6 and 4, 6 and 5, 6 and 6.

    a. What is the percent that both throws will be even numbers?
    b. What is the percent that the second throw is a 5?
    c. What is the percent that the first throw is lower than a 6?

2. You have the ability to choose three of your own classes, art, language, and physical education. There are three art classes (A1, A2, A3), two language classes (L1, L2), and two P.E. classes (P1, P2) to choose from. The order does not matter and you must choose one from each subject.

A1, L1, P1	A2, L1, P1	A3, L1, P1
A1, L1, P2	A2, L1, P2	A3, L1, P2
A1, L2, P1	A2, L2, P1	A3, L2, P1
A1, L2, P2	A2, L2, P2	A3, L2, P2

    Compare the percent of possibilities with A1 in your schedule to the percent of possibilities with L1 in your schedule.

Lesson 18:   Counting Problems

© 2015 Great Minds. eureka-math.org
G7-M3M4-SE-B2-1.3.1-02.2016

3. Fridays are selected to show your school pride. The colors of your school are orange, blue, and white, and you can show your spirit by wearing a top, a bottom, and an accessory with the colors of your school. During lunch, 11 students are chosen to play for a prize on stage. The table charts what the students wore.

Top	W	O	W	O	B	W	B	B	W	W	W
Bottom	B	O	B	B	O	B	B	B	O	W	B
Accessory	W	O	B	W	B	O	B	W	O	O	O

a. What is the percent of outfits that are one color?

b. What is the percent of outfits that include orange accessories?

4. Shana wears two rings (G represents gold, and S represents silver) at all times on her hand. She likes fiddling with them and places them on different fingers (pinky, ring, middle, index) when she gets restless. The chart is tracking the movement of her rings.

	Pinky Finger	Ring Finger	Middle Finger	Index Finger
Position 1		G	S	
Position 2			S	G
Position 3	G		S	
Position 4				S,G
Position 5	S	G		
Position 6	G	S		
Position 7	S		G	
Position 8	G		S	
Position 9		S,G		
Position 10		G	S	
Position 11			G	S
Position 12		S		G
Position 13	S,G			
Position 14			S,G	

a. What percent of the positions shows the gold ring on her pinky finger?

b. What percent of the positions shows both rings on the same finger?

5. Use the coordinate plane below to answer the following questions.

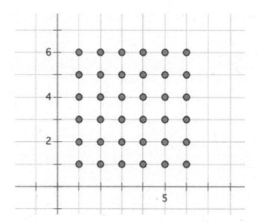

a. What is the percent of the 36 points whose quotient of $\dfrac{x\text{-coordinate}}{y\text{-coordinate}}$ is greater than one?

b. What is the percent of the 36 points whose coordinate quotient is equal to one?

© 2015 Great Minds. eureka-math.org
G7-M3M4-SE-B2-1.3.1-02.2016